200 Bedtime Stories

THE HOUSE ON THE HILL

It's very early in the morning on January 1st.
In the house on the hill, everyone is still asleep.
Everyone except little John and his sister Lisa.
The children tiptoe down the stairs.
Lisa opens the door to the living room.
Empty glasses and dark green bottles sit on the table.
Some bowls of salty crisps and nuts are on the table too.
They go over to a calendar that Mummy bought a while ago. It's a big one, with beautiful coloured pictures.
Mummy told the children that on New Year's Day they could turn the cover over and see the first picture.
Lisa grabs the calendar, then sits down next to her brother on the sofa.
On the cover is a nice clown with a funny hat and a red nose.

'How pretty,' says John.
They look at the picture for a long time.
Lisa grabs the bowl of nuts from the coffee table. She puts it between them.
They start to eat the nuts.
'How nice! It's New Year's Day!' says Lisa.
'Yippee!' exclaims John. 'When will it be New Year's Day again?'
'It takes a long time. A whole year. Why?'
'Do we have to wait that long to see the next picture?' asks John, with a sad face.
'Oh, no. We can do that next month.'
John takes a nut from the bowl.
'…and is a month a long time?'
'Not as long as a year.'
'Shall we get up early again?'
Lisa takes a nut from the bowl and crunches it.
'Maybe so….'

JACK FROST

It's been cold for a few days.

John, Lisa and Daddy run to the pond at the bottom of the hill. They are wearing mittens and warm scarves.

When John sees the frozen pond, he stops. The water has got hard....

'Jack Frost has done that,' explains Daddy. 'He changed the water into ice overnight.'

A little later, John steps on the ice. It's slippery and hard.

With tiny steps, he walks further on the frozen pond.

Boom! He falls on his bottom.

It doesn't hurt, because he's got thick trousers on. The ice is cold.

Daddy helps John up.

'Shall I push you around?' asks Daddy.

John holds his feet still, and Daddy slides him over the slippery ice.

'This is fun!' laughs John, sliding along.

After Lisa plays for a while, she comes trotting back with an icicle.

'Here's an ice lolly for you,' she says, and gives it to John.

John sucks on the cold icicle. It tastes just like water.

After they have played for a while, it is time to go home. Night is coming.

On the way home it begins to snow. Thick flakes drift out of the grey sky.

The children hold their mouths open and try their best to catch them.

'Sweets from the sky,' laughs John.

When they get home, Daddy helps John get out of his warm clothing.

'Did you have fun?' he asks.

'Yeeesss,' answers John, quickly, '...but Daddy?'

'Yes, son?'

'I think Jack Frost is a nice man. Can he come and play with us again tomorrow?'

Daddy laughs and ruffles John's hair. 'Of course.'

WHITENESS

Today everything is white: The grass, the trees, the house on the hill and all the other houses in the village. A thick blanket of snow covers the whole land.

John and Lisa have been very busy. They've built a snowman in the garden. He's not quite done, because he still needs a face.

Lisa looks for some pebbles to make his mouth and eyes.

'Beautiful,' says John. 'But he still doesn't have a nose. What can we use to make it?'

'We'll ask Mummy for a carrot,' answers Lisa.

Mummy is making soup in the kitchen.

'Mummy, may we have a carrot please?'

'Oooh,' says Mummy, 'I just put our last carrot into the soup.'

'But…now we won't have a nose for our snow-man,' says Lisa, disappointed.

'I'm sorry, darling,' says Mummy. 'The only thing I have is this cucumber.'

'A cucumber? But Mummy, snowmen don't usually have cucumber noses, do they?'

'No,' laughs Mummy, 'but your snowman is not an ordinary snowman, is he?'

'No?' ask the children, surprised.

'No, I think your snowman is very, very special. I think he should have a cucumber nose.'

'Really?' asks Lisa doubtfully.

A little later, a beautiful snowman with a very special nose stands in the garden. With the best nose a snowman ever had. At least that's what Lisa and John think.

SLEDGING

'Shall we go sledging?' asks Lisa.

'Yeeesss!' yells John, happily.

A little later they are standing in the snow in their warm jackets.

They fly down the hill, screaming with happiness. When they get to the bottom, they pull the sledge back to the top and get ready to go again.

But then Carl comes by. Carl is an annoying boy who always thinks he knows best.

'Hey,' he calls, while he climbs up the hill to where John and Lisa are ready with the sledge. 'Shall I teach you how to go sledging?'

'We already know how. Watch!'

John and Lisa get on the sledge and zoom down the hill.

'You idiots!' yells Carl. 'You don't know anything about it.'

John and Lisa look at Carl angrily. They pull the sledge back up the hill.

'Just let me show you how you really do it,' says Carl as he grabs the rope from their hands.

Carl flops on the sledge on his tummy.

'When you go like this you go much faster. Give me a push.'

Lisa gives the sledge a push and off goes Carl. The sledge races down the hill. Carl screams and waves his arms.

'That's how you have to do it!' he cries.

But the sledge runs into a branch. Carl flies off the sledge into the deep snow. When he scrambles out, he is covered with snow. There's snow inside his jacket and it feels cold. He tries to brush it out, but can't. John and Lisa roll on the ground, laughing. Carl runs away as fast as he can.

It will be a long time before he tries to teach anyone another lesson!

FEEDING THE BIRDS

John looks through the kitchen window at the snow.

A lonely little bird is looking for food in the snow. Mummy sees it too.

'Shall we give the poor thing something to eat?' asks Mummy.

John nods.

'I have some bread crusts left. We can make a nice meal out of them for that hungry little bird.'

Pretty soon there's a little pile of crumbs and nuts on the kitchen table.

Mummy gets a pack of butter out.

'Look,' she says, 'now you can mix the crumbs and nuts with the butter and make a ball.'

'Why should we do that, Mummy?' John wants to know.

'Otherwise the crumbs will blow away. This way they'll stick in the butter. Birds really love butter.'

John gets to work. The slippery butter feels funny on his fingers, but soon the ball is ready.

Mummy takes the ball that John has made and puts it in a net bag.

She hangs the net bag on a bush outside.

A bit later, John looks out the window. He sees that the curious bird has already flown to the

butterball.

The bird looks at the strange thing on the bush. Carefully, he pecks at it with his beak.

Then suddenly he flies away.

'Doesn't he think it tastes good?' John asks himself, disappointed.

But then the bird comes back. It has brought along two friends. The hungry birds begin to peck away at the butterball.

John beams with happiness to see the birds fill their tummies.

He has three new little friends!

THAW

The Christmas holiday is over.

John and Lisa have to go back to school today. The sun has shone all day and it is warm outside.

When school is over, John and Lisa rush home. They run as fast as they can to see their snowman again.

As they arrive, they see that the snow has begun to melt. Here and there they see big holes in the carpet of snow.

He's tipping a bit and big drops are dripping from his cucumber nose. But he still has a big smile.

'Mummy, Mummy, the snowman is melting!' calls Lisa to her mother, who wants to go indoors.

'Our lovely snowman,' says John sadly.

The cucumber nose falls to the ground with a soft thud.

'What a pity,' says Mummy. 'He was such a lovely snowman. But that's the way it is with snowmen. They don't last long. As soon as the sun sees them, they go away fast.'

'Where do they go?' Lisa wants to know.

Mummy thinks it over.

'To the North Pole. Up there it's really cold the whole year. The snowmen like that a lot.'

'Do they live there?' asks John, surprised.

'Yes, in beautiful snow-houses, in a snow village,' says Mummy.

'A snow village?' The children look at Mummy in surprise. John rubs his nose.

'Mummy, do they have post boxes?'

'I think so. Why do you ask?'

'Can we send our snowman a letter?'

'Oh, sure you can,' laughs Mummy.

'Shall we write one?'

'Yes!' shout the children, and they run inside.

Outside, the snowman laughs for the last time.

Then he falls apart.

Bye, snowman – until next year!

AUNTIE FRAN

Today Auntie Fran is coming to visit. John and Lisa know Auntie Fran all too well. She is an annoying, fat aunt of their father's. She always comes to visit around New Year's. She eats tons of cakes and biscuits. When everything is gone, she waddles home like a blown-up balloon.

The children think Auntie Fran is ter-ri-ble.

'She has an awful sweet tooth,' says Lisa to her little brother.

'Yes, and she always gives us horrible, dirty, sticky sweets that have been sitting in her handbag forever,' answers John.

Lisa makes an ugly face.

'I can't bear to think about those wet kisses she gives us. And always on the mouth. Ugh!'

Chills run up her back.

'We've got to come up with a plan, John,' says Lisa. 'Otherwise it will be awful.'

Just then Lisa spots a red pen.

'Wait,' she says, 'I have an idea….'

In a short while the doorbell rings. Auntie Fran is here.

After she gives Mummy and Daddy a sticky, wet kiss, she asks, 'And where are those darling children?'

'They are playing in their room,' says Mummy. 'Children, come give your Auntie Fran a kiss.'

In a moment John and Lisa are downstairs. Their faces and hands are covered with red spots. 'What's the matter with you, children?' cries Auntie Fran, terrified. 'Oh my! Have you caught the measles?'

John and Lisa nod.

'Well then, ah…,' gasps Auntie Fran, 'you'd better not give me a kiss. You should go to bed right now.'

'What a pity, Auntie Fran,' says Lisa. 'But okay. See you soon.'

Happily they run upstairs.

Yippee! No Auntie Fran this year!

NOSEY

black and has a very twitchy nose and white paws. Very carefully, the children pet him. The puppy looks at his new friends with sparkling eyes.

'Hello,' says Lisa to the pup. 'What's your name?'

'Good question. He doesn't have one yet,' says Daddy. 'What shall we call him?' John and Lisa think it over carefully.

'Blackie!' shouts John.

'That's what Farmer Pete calls his dog,' says Mummy. 'Can you think of another name?'

'Nosey!' exclaims Lisa. 'Because he looks like he wants to poke his nose into everything!'

Everybody thinks that's a great name. Nosey too, because he begins to bark happily.

Daddy comes home. He has a big brown box with him. Carefully, he sets the box on the ground.

'John and Lisa,' calls Mummy, 'come quickly. Daddy has a surprise for you.'

The children, who were playing upstairs, come running down.

They see the big brown box.

'What's inside?' asks Lisa.

'Take a look,' says Daddy.

Together they look in the box. Inside sits an adorable puppy.

'Oooh! What a cutie!' shout the children.

Mummy takes the puppy out of the box. He is

A little later a cosy basket is set by the fire. Mummy puts Nosey in it. But Nosey doesn't want to stay in the basket.

He spots a little ball and begins to play with it. John and Lisa play with him.

They think their new friend is a fantastic present.

MITTENS

Nosey lies snoring in his basket by the fire. He is really tired from all the romping with his new friends. Lisa and John decide to play outside so they won't wake him up.

The wind is cold. John wants to put on his red mittens, but he can't find them.

'Mummy, do you know where my mittens are?'

'No, dear. When did you wear them last?'

'This morning, when we took Nosey for a little walk,' says Lisa, who wants to go out. 'After that I saw them on the floor by the coat hooks.'

John and Mummy look in the hall, but the mittens aren't there.

'Then we'll have to look really hard for them,' grumbles Mummy. 'Sometimes you're a bit of a messy one.'

They look in the hall, but the mittens aren't there.

Then they look in the living room. They aren't there either.

'What's that in Nosey's basket?' asks Mummy.

John looks at the sleeping puppy. Beside Nosey there's a lot of red stuff. The same red stuff that John's mittens are made of. Or rather, were made of, because Nosey has torn them all apart!

'My red mittens…,' wails John.

Mummy is a little angry at Nosey. But the sleeping puppy looks so cute that her anger disappears. Nosey just thought the mittens were toys. John should have put them in the closet.

'From now on you will have to put all your things away, you two,' says Mummy, 'because this little rascal in the basket will do whatever he wants with them.'

'I will do that, Mummy. Promise.'

DIARY

Daddy is cleaning his office. A huge pile of paper and other stuff sits there, ready to fall over. Daddy is a messy one sometimes, just like John.

Lisa comes by. 'Hello, Daddy,' she says.

'Hello, Lisa,' says Daddy.

'It's about time that you clean up a bit,' laughs Lisa.

Then she sees an old notebook. 'Are you going to throw this away?' she asks.

Daddy looks at the notebook.

'Would you like to have it? Be my guest,' he says.

Lisa rushes to her room with the notebook. She sits down at her desk and picks her best pen out of her school bag.

'I can use this notebook as my diary. Or as a poetry book. Or both,' she thinks.

She begins to write in big letters.

Lisa is my name,
And John is my brother.
I like to eat bananas.
I get them from my mother.

Our house is pretty big,
It sits upon a hill.
Below the sheep say 'Baaa.'
At night it's very still.

Peter owns the sheep.
His farm is lots of fun.
We love to go and visit.
And play out in the sun.

We'll take our puppy with us,
That little rascal, Nosey.
He'll love to meet the sheep,
And it will be so cosy.

We'll visit Mrs Holly.
She has a little shop.
If we can buy a lolly,
We'll taste it while we stop.

I've got to go to sleep.
It's late and I hear Mummy.
Tomorrow I'll get a sweet,
And smile and rub my tummy.

POST

Lisa looks out of the window. She's watching the post box. She sees the postman's truck coming down the road.

She runs outside. Are there letters for her in the post box? Lisa wriggles impatiently, waiting to see what the post will bring.

A few days ago Lisa emptied the post box. There were some letters in it, but they were for Mummy and Daddy. Not one for Lisa.

'I never get a letter,' she complained. 'So why doesn't anybody write to me?'

Then she had an idea. If she wrote someone a letter, then maybe they would write back....

First she made a list of people that she wanted to write to.

Grannie and Grandad, Uncle Bob and Aunt Bonnie, Auntie Fran…? No, not Auntie Fran. Her friends Julie and Nellie. She especially shouldn't forget them.

Oh yes, Farmer Pete and Mrs Holly from the little shop.

As soon as her list was done, Lisa began to write. She did her very best not to make any mistakes. She wrote letter after letter.

When all the letters were written, she looked for envelopes and stamps. Lisa stuck the letters into the envelopes and wrote the addresses on them. Then she glued them shut and stuck a stamp on each one.

So the job was done. The letters could go to the post.

Yikes! The postman's truck stops at their door.

'Hello, Lisa,' laughs the postman. 'I have a whole lot of letters for you.'

Lisa takes the letters inside, laughing, and begins to read them.

'It's so nice to get post,' she thinks.

CHINA DAY

It's China Day in John's classroom.

All week long, the children have done things that have to do with China. They have drawn a lovely Chinese dragon and made wonderful Chinese paper lanterns.

Since it's the last day of the week, the children have got all their Chinese things ready.

Everybody is wearing colourful paper Chinese hats that they made.

Today they will eat as the Chinese do.

With chopsticks.

Their teacher has brought chopsticks for everyone.

'How can you eat with these things?' asks John, while he looks at them.

'Shall we give it a try?' asks the teacher. She sets a little bowl in front of each person. In each bowl there are three sour gummy bear sweets.

'People in China often eat rice, but we will eat our sour bears. They will be a little easier. Try it.'

The children give it a try. My, it's hard! There's lots of laughing. They find it goes best if they stab the bears with the chopsticks.

Finally everyone has gobbled up their bears.

'You have learned how real Chinese people eat, but can you write like them?' asks the teacher.

The children look at each other with surprise.

'How do Chinese people write?' John wants to know.

'They use pictures to say things instead of letters. Can each of you draw a picture of something that makes you happy?' The children start drawing.

When they are done, the teacher asks John to show his drawing.

'More sour bears would make me very happy!' John laughs.

The children clap and cheer as the teacher give each one another bear.

FAIRY TALE

'John, shall we play Little Red Riding Hood?' asks Lisa.

'No,' says John. 'I'd rather play Sleeping Beauty. Then I can be the prince and come to wake you up.'

'But I would rather play Little Red Riding Hood,' insists Lisa.

'No,' says John loudly. 'It's Sleeping Beauty or I won't play with you.'

'Okay then,' Lisa gives in. 'We'll play Sleeping Beauty.'

Lisa puts on her crown and an old dress of Mummy's. John puts on an old hat. A fly swat-

ter is his sword.

The Princess lies down on a bench. 'I'm lying here sleeping, waiting for my prince to come and wake me up.'

'Wait, Princess, I'm coming to wake you,' yells John as he wildly brandishes his fly swatter.

'It would be nice if the Prince is a little more careful,' says Mummy as she comes through the room. 'You almost knocked down my beautiful vase.'

'Sorry, Mummy,' says John. But as soon as Mummy is out of the room, he goes on swinging wildly.

'I'm hacking my way through the thorn bushes. Chop-chop!'

Out of the corner of her eye the Princess watches the Prince.

'Chop-chop,' continues the Prince. Everything in his way gets a swat from the fly swatter.

Finally the Prince reaches the Princess.

'So… you're freed,' he says, panting from all his work.

'Hey Prince, you have to kiss me,' whispers the Princess. She pushes her lips out for a kiss.

The Prince doesn't know what to do.

Hesitating, he bends over. He stares at the Princess's lips.

'Uh…,' he stammers. 'If you like, we can play Little Red Riding Hood….'

THE HAT

It's stormy outside. The wind blows fat streaks of rain against the windows. Tick, tick, tick. Despite the bad weather, John and Lisa are going to take Nosey for a walk. They have on their raincoats and boots on. That way they'll stay nice and dry. Lisa has a hat on. Nosey doesn't have a raincoat. He has no trouble with wind and rain. But he does have a collar and lead. That way he will stay near the children.

Suddenly the wind plucks the hat off Lisa's head. It flies through the air.

Lisa tries to grab her hat, but the wind blows it farther away. She runs after it. Nosey runs after her. He pulls on his lead and drags John along with him.

Oooh! Lisa falls down. John, who is hanging on to Nosey's lead, can't stop. He falls on top of his sister.

'Ow!' yells Lisa. 'Ow!' yells John.

Nosey runs ahead with his lead flapping behind him.

'Nosey!' yells John, but the puppy doesn't hear him. In a split second, Nosey disappears in the rain.

Now they've lost the hat and Nosey.

'Oh, we've got to go find him,' says Lisa, frightened.

'Where should we look?' asks John.

'Maybe your hat is in another country by now.' Lisa and John don't know what to do.

'Woof-woof!' they suddenly hear. Astonished, they look around.

It's Nosey!

He's got the hat. Nosey gives it back to Lisa, panting. 'How nice of you, Nosey,' says Lisa, delighted. She gives him a big hug. It doesn't matter that Nosey is soaking wet and completely covered with mud. Sweet, sweet Nosey.

SHOPPING LIST

'Lisa, dear' says Mummy, 'please run over to Mrs Holly's shop. Get six apples, a bag of flour, a package of butter, and three eggs. Can you re- member all that?'

'Of course I can remember that,' brags Lisa. 'Six apples, a bag of flour, a pack of butter, and three eggs.'

'Great,' says Mummy.

Lisa sets off.

She likes to go to Mrs Holly's shop. She always gets to pick out a sweet. Which kind will she pick? Yummy red cherry sweets, or the yellow gummy worms that you can wrap around your finger? Or maybe just a lollipop? Or a big ball of bubble gum?

Her mouth waters. She walks a little faster, because she wants to pop a sweet in her mouth as soon as possible.

Aha, there's the shop. When Lisa opens the door, a little bell rings: 'Ding-a-ling!'

'Hello, Lisa,' says Mrs Holly. 'What will it be today?'

Lisa wants to remember Mummy's shopping list, but.... Oh dear, she's been thinking so hard about sweets that she's forgotten the list.

'Um… ah,' stammers Lisa.

'What's the matter?' asks Mrs Holly. 'Have you forgotten what you need to bring back?'

Lisa nods, embarrassed. Her cheeks get red.

Mrs Holly laughs. 'Your mother gave me the list over the phone,' she says, 'just in case you forgot anything.'

She gives Lisa a bag with all the things. Lisa takes the bag and starts to leave.

'Aren't you forgetting something?' she hears Mrs Holly ask.

Lisa turns around.

'Your sweet….'

SLIPPERY

'We live on a hill,' boasts Lisa to her school-mates. 'From my window I can see all the houses in the village.'

'That must be nice,' says Julie. She is impressed.

'When it snows, we can ride our sledge from the garden to the bottom,' continues Lisa.

Her friends are very jealous of her. Lisa is proud because she lives on the only hill in the area.

A while later school is over.

'Be very careful, because it's slippery as glass outside,' says the teacher.

Lisa steps outside and almost slips and falls. But she stays on her feet. Wow, it is really slippery!

Later, Lisa, John and Mummy walk home, taking tiny steps. John and Lisa hold tight to Mummy's hands.

Then they come to the hill. At the top stands their house. It's nice and warm up there.

They start walking up the path.

Hey, what's happening? They are sliding down!

The path is so slippery that they can't go up.

They try again. But again they slide back down.

'Watch,' says Lisa, getting ready. 'I'll take a run at it.' She steps back a little and then begins to run. But just before she starts up the hill, she slips. Boom, she falls on her backside.

Then she tries climbing up on her hands and knees. That works better. But in a few minutes she slides back to the bottom again.

John and Mummy stand next to the path. They try walking on the grass up to the top. That works!

Lisa follows them. Boy, it's hard to live at the top of a hill!

PIGGY BANKS

Lisa has a little box. It's an old, metal cigar box. She keeps her coins in that box. She earns them when she helps Daddy wash the car. Or if she helps Mummy wash up the dishes. If she shakes the box, the coins inside make a lovely sound.

One day Lisa and Mummy go shopping at Mrs Holly's shop. There's a lovely pink piggy bank on the shelf. It smiles at Lisa.

'That pig oinks if you put a coin in its mouth,' says Mrs Holly.

'It would be much nicer to save my coins in that than in a metal box,' thinks Lisa.

She wants to buy the piggy.

'Mummy, may I buy that piggy?' she asks.

Lisa has brought along her metal box with all her savings. Mummy counts the money for her. She has enough to buy the piggy.

Mrs Holly takes the piggy from the shelf and sets it on the counter.

'So, dear, you have more than you need.' She gives Lisa one coin back.

Lisa sticks the coin in her new piggy bank.

'Oink!' says the pig. 'Ting-a-ling,' goes the coin as it drops into the bank. It sounds empty with just one coin inside.

But Lisa has a plan already.

Soon she's going to help Mummy with the dishes. Then the piggy will sound a little fuller.

STORM

'Tonight we will have a big storm,' says the weatherman on the telly.

As Lisa lies in bed, she thinks about what the weatherman said. She hears the wind rising again. With angry blasts, it blows against the house on the hill. Lisa snuggles deeper under the blanket. She hopes the house is strong enough.

Suddenly the door of her room swings open. It is John.

'Lisa, can I get in your bed? I can't sleep. The wind is scaring me.'

'Of course, come on,' says Lisa.

They snuggle close, listening to the wind, a little scared.

Then they hear a crack and a boom. Something has fallen.

John squeezes Lisa's hand hard. 'Pretty soon our house is going to blow away,' he says, shivering.

'Imagine that our house flies away. Who knows where we would land?' Lisa says. 'Maybe we'd fly over the ocean. Then we could see a whale or an octopus out of the window.'

'Or a pirate ship,' adds John.

'Maybe we'd land on a desert island with palm trees,' says Lisa.

'A pirate island! Maybe with buried treasure, Lisa.'

'Oh, yes, and then we find it. Maybe there's a crown in it. Then I'd be the queen and you'd be my knight. Or would you rather be a prince?'

John doesn't answer. He's fallen asleep, thinking about these fantasies.

'We'll see about that,' says Lisa. She holds her brother's hand tight.

Later the two dream about their desert island in the ocean, while the storm rages on.

Broken Arm

All the children in the class are crowding around Timmy.

Timmy has broken his arm. There's a heavy cast on it.

The children are drawing pictures on Timmy's cast. Now it is John's turn. He draws a pig. He's good at that.

'It must be fun to have a cast like that,' he says to his friend. 'I want one too. Then you can draw on my arm.'

'It hurt a lot when I broke my arm,' says Timmy. 'I cried a lot.'

That scares John a bit. Pain is no fun.

Still, he feels a little jealous over the cast.

Later Timmy's arm feels itchy. He wants to scratch, but he can't because of his cast. The itchiness won't stop. Timmy is going crazy from it.

The teacher comes up with an idea. She carefully slides a thin stick between the cast and Timmy's arm.

Now Timmy can scratch his arm.

'Ha-ha-ha,' laughs Timmy, delighted.

John watches Timmy the whole time. He thinks a cast isn't so nice now.

Timmy is bothered. It must be annoying if he can't scratch.

During the break Timmy stays in the classroom. He is afraid that someone might bump into his painful arm. Through the window he watches his friends playing outside.

He sits quietly on the chair, because he doesn't want to break anything else.

THE GARDEN SHED

What a disaster! The storm last week has blown down the shed in the garden. There are boards all over the place.

The children help Daddy clean up. They lay the boards in a pile. 'We can use them as firewood,' says Daddy.

'Say, what do you think? Shall we build a new shed to replace the old one?'

The children love the idea.

They go together in the car to buy a lot of wood and nails.

Back home, Daddy begins to hammer and saw. John and Lisa help him.

'Could you please bring me a new board?' asks Daddy. 'Who can hold it steady for me? I need more nails.'

They work the whole day through. Towards evening the shed is done.

Mummy comes home. She's been away visiting a friend all day.

'What a fine shed,' she cries, astonished. 'My, you have worked hard.'

The children and Daddy nod proudly.

Mummy walks around the shed, admiring it. 'It's really nice. But I wonder….'

'What?' ask Daddy and the children.

They have been so busy pounding and cutting that they have forgotten to make a door. How silly! Now nobody can get in.

The children are disappointed, but Mummy laughs and tries to cheer them up.

'I was visiting my friend Monica. She gave me a lovely chocolate cake. Shall we taste it?'

A little later the children are at the table with big slices of chocolate cake. And the door of the shed? They've already forgotten it.

They can just make the door tomorrow.

THE ROOSTER

Daddy has been to visit Farmer Pete and has brought home three hens and a rooster. Beside the shed he's made a little chicken pen from wire and posts.

When he comes home, he puts the chickens and rooster in the pen. The hens begin to walk around. The rooster stands perfectly still. He looks around the pen suspiciously.

'You need to give them some food right away,' says Daddy to John and Lisa.

The chicken feed is in the garden shed. The children scoop a bit out into a blue bucket.

Nosey comes running over. When John and Lisa go in the pen, he wants to come with them.

'You may come in if you promise to be good,' says Lisa.

Nosey barks.

'Okay,' says Lisa, and she lets Nosey into the pen. The dog looks at the chickens.

John and Lisa scatter some chicken feed on the ground. The hens peck at the grains with their beaks.

Nosey goes cautiously over to them. He sniffs them. They don't pay attention to Nosey. They are too busy with the food.

After a moment the rooster comes over. Like a proud king, he walks slowly, with his head high. He starts to eat.

Nosey comes near him. The rooster looks at Nosey fiercely.

'I wouldn't sniff him, Nosey. I think he won't like that,' says Lisa.

But Nosey doesn't listen.

Suddenly the rooster pecks Nosey hard on the nose.

'Yelp, yelp, yelp!' howls Nosey, as he runs away.

Well, Nosey, that's what you get for not listening well.

SICK

John has been sick for two days. Yesterday he slept a lot, but today he feels a little better and can watch telly.

Lisa is not sick and has to go to school. She is a bit jealous of her little brother!

The next day Lisa has to get up early and go to school. John gets to stay home. Jealously, Lisa thinks, 'He can watch telly all day, and….' Suddenly she has an idea.

'Mummy,' Lisa whinges, 'I don't feel so good. I have a very bad headache.'

Mummy looks at her, a bit concerned.

'That's too bad, sweetie. Shall I take your temperature?'

Lisa nods sadly and crawls into bed. Mummy comes with the thermometer.

'Here, hold this under your tongue,' she says.

Lisa does her best to look very sick.

'Ping, ping,' goes the thermometer in a moment.

Mummy takes it and looks at the numbers.

'No fever,' she says. 'I'll get you some medicine for your headache. Then you'll feel better soon.'

Oh, dear, her plan isn't going right. She needs to try something else.

'Mummy, I have a tummy ache,' she whimpers, rubbing it.

'Then I'll get you something for your stomach ache,' replies Mummy gently.

Oh, dear, it's going all wrong again.

'Ow, something's hurting my ear,' she starts again.

Mummy raises an eyebrow and looks at Lisa sternly.

'I think you aren't sick at all. I think you're perfectly healthy. So healthy that you can wash up the dishes the rest of the week, if you keep on pretending.'

Soon after that, Lisa is in class. Today they are doing craft projects. She loves that. She's pretty happy she isn't sick!

ANNOYING

'What awful weather. Stay inside as long as you can,' says Daddy to the children.

What a pity. John and Lisa really wanted to go out to play, and make a camp or something. But big, fat raindrops keep falling.

They sit in the living room. They are completely bored and restless.

Daddy laughs at the sighing children.

'I know a great game for rainy days like this one,' he says.

The children perk up immediately.

'Shall we make a picture book?'

John and Lisa stare at Daddy in surprise.

'You know,' says Daddy, 'a story book with nice pictures you make yourselves. When we have it all done, we'll put it inside a cover and you'll have a real story book.'

Make a book? That sounds like fun!

Lisa and John go off looking for coloured pencils and paper.

'But Daddy,' asks Lisa, 'what should the book be about?'

'What do you think about Princess Annie and the dragon that only eats strawberry ice cream?' John and Lisa look at each other and burst out laughing.

Lisa makes up the story and writes a bit of it on each page. John makes a nice picture to go with each page.

After a few hours of hard work, their book is almost done. It's really nice. Daddy makes a beautiful cover for it and puts the pages inside it. When it's bedtime, John and Lisa get to pick out a book to read.

You can guess what book they choose that night!

AT THE BARBER'S

John is at the barber shop.

The barber grabs the electric shaver and gets set to start cutting John's hair.

'Ding-dong!' A new customer comes in.

'Oh, no,' thinks John. 'It's that annoying boy, Carl.'

'You'll have to wait,' says the barber. 'Please take a seat.'

The barber begins to cut John's hair. 'Buzz,' goes the shaver. 'Hold your head still,' says the barber, 'or else you'll wind up with a bald spot on your head.'

That gives Carl a naughty idea.

'I'm going to make John laugh,' he thinks. 'If he moves his head, the barber will make a bald spot. That will be funny.'

Carl begins to make silly faces. John acts like he doesn't see him.

'Oh, rats,' thinks Carl, as he sees that his plan isn't working.

John is done. He gets a lolly because he was so good.

While John puts his jacket on, Carl goes to the barber's chair and sits down. 'Hold your head still,' says the barber, 'or else you'll wind up with a bald spot on your head.'

He turns on the shaver and begins to work on Carl's hair.

'Bye,' says John.

'Bye,' says the barber.

Carl still wants to make a funny face at John. He turns his head suddenly.

'What are you doing?' cries the barber. The shaver has cut a bald spot on Carl's head.

Carl looks at himself in the mirror.

A bald strip runs through his hair.

Dumb, dumb Carl.

COCK-A-DOODLE-DOO!

It is the middle of the night. In the house on top of the hill nobody can sleep. Except John. He sleeps through anything.

Daddy, Mummy and Lisa sit in the kitchen.

'Cock-a-doodle-doo!' they hear.

'What makes that rooster crow in the middle of the night? We can't sleep!' grumbles Daddy.

'Maybe he thinks it's getting light outside,' suggests Lisa.

'It's midnight. It'll be hours before it gets light.'

'What can we do?' Mummy asks.

Daddy thinks it over. 'I will take care of this.' He puts on his jacket and goes outside.

Lisa hears him yelling at the rooster.

'And?' asks Mummy when he comes back in.

'The chickens are also awake now, so I don't think that helped much.'

Daddy just finishes saying this when they hear another 'Cock-a-doodle-doo!'

He sits down helplessly on his chair. 'Oh, I'm so tired!' he sighs.

Then Lisa has an idea.

'If we can't stop the rooster from crowing, then we have to stop ourselves from hearing him crow.'

'And how are you going to do that? Sleep all

night long with your fingers in your ears?' asks Daddy sleepily.

Lisa goes to the bathroom. In a moment she returns. She has a couple of cottonwool balls with her.

She gives Daddy and Mummy two apiece.

'Stick these in your ears,' she says.

'Fantastic,' yells Daddy, after he stuffs the cotton wool in his ears. 'I don't hear the rooster any more!'

'What did you say?' asks Mummy.

After that everyone goes to bed for a nice night's sleep.

DAVEY

'Ding-dong,' sounds the door bell.

It's Monica, Mummy's friend. She has to go away for the day and has asked if Mummy could look after her baby, Davey, for her.

A little later Lisa sits on the chair with Davey on her lap. 'Now I'm a real mummy,' she thinks.

When it's time for Davey's bottle, Lisa doesn't want Mummy to help. She has often given her dolly a bottle. Did she need Mummy's help then?

Davey has emptied the bottle.

'See,' says Lisa proudly.

Davey needs to be burped. She puts him up to her shoulder. She pats him gently on his back.

'See how well I can do it, Mummy?' she asks.

Mummy nods.

Suddenly Davey makes a loud burp.

But what is that?

Lisa looks at her shoulder. Davey has been sick. Ugh! Her t-shirt is all messy!

Lisa acts as if nothing has happened. She can handle this alone. After all, isn't she a little mother?

Then there's a loud 'Pffft!' sound.

Something smells! Lisa plugs her nose.

'I think Davey needs a clean nappy, Mummy,' she says.

Mummy sits still and looks at Lisa.

Suddenly it dawns on Lisa.

'Do I have to do that…?' she stammers.

Mummy nods, laughing. She lays out a clean nappy and some cleaning pads.

'You've done that for your dolly too, right?'

'Yes, but…this is real,' says Lisa, hesitating.

Mummy laughs. 'You know what? I'll take over. Because being a mummy can be hard work, don't you think?'

'Uh, yes,' sighs Lisa, relieved. 'That's a good idea.'

TINY ELF

Lisa and John are playing in the garden with Nosey.

Suddenly Nosey begins to bark. He's standing by a hole.

'What is it, Nosey?' asks John.

As they come a bit closer, they see that Nosey is barking at… an elf.

'Help!' cries the elf. 'I've fallen in this hole and can't get out.'

John and Lisa quickly help the elf climb out of the hole. He is only as tall as a glass of water.

'Thank you very much, children,' he says, obviously relieved. 'I am Tiny Elf. You are John and Lisa, right?'

The children look at the elf, amazed.

'How do you know our names?' asks Lisa.

The elf laughs. 'Actually, I live in your house.'

'In our house?' asks John, completely surprised. 'Where?'

'I live in your airing closet. It's always nice and warm there. Now and then I wander around your house and garden. I've already seen you two many times. That's how I know your names. Most of the time I hide, because I don't want to be bothered. But since you've saved me, you can always come visit me, any day. You just have to promise me one thing: you must not say anything to Mummy and Daddy. They surely won't believe you. Grownups don't be-lieve in elves.'

The children promise not to tell.

'So, now I need to get home. There's a pie baking in my oven. With any luck it's not burnt. Bye now!'

The tiny elf walks away.

'Bye!' call the children after him.

29

ELF PIES

John and Lisa sneak into the airing closet to pay Tiny Elf a visit.

'Pssst, Tiny Elf,' whispers Lisa. 'Are you home?'

It's silent. Then a tiny door in the wall opens.

'Well, hello, children,' laughs the elf.

'We came to see where you live,' says John.

'Right here,' laughs the elf. 'You came at just the right time. I've just baked lots of pies. I love them. If you like, you can eat some with me.'

Naturally the children want to do that. Tiny Elf rolls out a trolley loaded with pies. 'Help yourself!' he says.

The children start gobbling up the delicious pies.

But just then the airing closet door opens. It is Mummy. Tiny Elf dashes into his house again.

'What are you two doing here?' Mummy asks.

Then she sees the bulging mouths of the children.

'Now, just a minute,' she says, 'are you hiding in here, eating sweets? Oh, how naughty!' she cries angrily. John and Lisa look at each other.

'Mummy, dis ish not shweets,' John tries to explain with a full mouth. But Lisa nudges him. 'Shhh,' she says. 'We mush not shay anyshing....'

'Just come on, you rascals. I'm going to have to punish you,' says Mummy.

A while later, John and Lisa are standing in the corner.

But who's that sneaking up? It's Tiny Elf!

'Oh dear, oh dear,' he says. 'Your mummy was really angry. Maybe next time we'd better not have any pies, huh?'

John and Lisa look at Tiny Elf with disappointment.

'No, no – just a few, then…,' he laughs.

KITTENS

Farmer Pete has just called: His cat, Sparkle, has had kittens!

John and Lisa rush over to the farm. Nosey runs after them.

'The kittens are in the barn,' says Farmer Pete. 'Shall we go look at them? Nosey must stay here. He will scare Sparkle.'

Sparkle is lying there in the hay with her kittens.

There are four of them. They are so tiny!

'Why are their eyes shut?' asks Lisa.

'That's because they are just newly born,' answers Farmer Pete. 'In a few days their eyes will open.'

'Could I please hold one?' begs John.

'I don't think Sparkle will like that. Let her rest for a few days. Then you can cuddle the kittens as much as you want.'

The children can't take their eyes off the kittens. They are so cute!

But who is this running into the barn?

It's Nosey.

Curious, he runs to the children.

Suddenly Sparkle jumps up. She snarls and arches her back.

The children are terrified. Nosey is too.

He runs out as fast as he can.

'That was a scare,' breathes Lisa.

'That's the way Sparkle protects her little ones,' says Farmer Pete. 'Nosey won't try to come in here again.'

The children go with Farmer Pete to get food for Sparkle. Now that she's a mother, she must eat a lot. That way she can make lots of milk for her kittens. Then they will get bigger very quickly.

Lisa and John ask if they can come back tomorrow.

'Of course,' laughs Farmer Pete, 'but you must leave Nosey at home.'

Agreed!

UNCLE JOHN AND AUNTIE LISA

John and Lisa are going to visit Sparkle and her kittens again today. They can't touch them, but they can look.

'Hello, Sparkle,' says Lisa softly. 'May we look at your babies?'

'Meow,' answers Sparkle.

John and Lisa lie down in front of Sparkle's nest in the hay.

There are two striped kittens and two black ones. My, they are cute!

Farmer Pete comes into the barn.

'Aha! Uncle John and Auntie Lisa are here! I hadn't seen you.'

'We aren't your aunt and uncle,' laughs Lisa.

'No, not mine,' says Farmer Pete. 'But maybe you would like to be aunt and uncle to Sparkle's kittens.'

'Oh, that would be great,' say the children.

'Shall I ask Sparkle if she would like that?'

The children quickly nod yes.

Farmer Pete goes to Sparkle and scratches her head.

'Sparkle, would you like it if these two fine children become aunt and uncle to your kittens?'

Sparkle tips her head and looks at John and Lisa. Then she meows and begins to purr.

'Well, I think she likes the idea.'

'Congratulations, Auntie Lisa and Uncle John,' says Farmer Pete.

John and Lisa are proud!

'Say, would you like to celebrate this happy news with a piece of pie?' Farmer Pete doesn't have to ask twice. Auntie Lisa and Uncle John run out of the barn, laughing.

Later Farmer Pete brings a little piece of fish to Sparkle.

In all the excitement, we can't forget the mother cat....

FOG

Today it's very foggy.

John and Lisa look out the window. The garden, trees, chicken coop…everything is gone! They see only the white fog that hides everything.

It's time to go to school. As they go outside, it's very still. John and Lisa look at each other and stand quietly. John takes Mummy's hand, because he's a little scared of the fog.

They walk carefully along the path down the hill. At the bottom of the hill is the post box. John knows that very well. But no matter how hard he looks, he can't see it.

'Mummy, the fog has eaten up our post box,' he says.

Mummy laughs. 'Oh dear, then we'll have to get another one.'

John looks to see if the tree is still standing on the other side of the street.

No, the tree is gone too. Wow, the fog is greedy, eating everything up.

Then he turns to try to see the house. Oh, no – the house has completely disappeared.

'Mummy, our house is…gone too,' stammers John, looking at the place where the house used to be.

'Then we'll get another house as well,' laughs Mummy. Lisa laughs too.

John doesn't understand. The house is gone, but Mummy isn't scared.

Silently, they walk further in the mysterious fog.

Finally, there's the school.

'Luckily the fog hasn't eaten up our school,' John says to Mummy.

'Don't be afraid, John. The fog will be gone soon and everything will be just as before.'

'Will our house be back too?'

Mummy laughs and gives John a big kiss.

'Yes, John, for sure.'

FELIX THE ODD-JOB MAN

Everybody in town loves Felix, the odd-job man. He's not very young any more, but he is the best repair man around.

Mummy asked Felix if he will build a chest of drawers for her.

'Of course,' answered Felix.

The next day Felix's van stops in front of the house on the hill.

Felix pulls the chest out of the van and brings it into the house.

'What a nice chest!' cries Mummy delightedly.

'Thanks,' replies Felix proudly.

Later everyone is sitting at the kitchen table, happily eating a chocolate cake.

Felix tells funny stories, making Mummy and the children laugh.

Then Mummy takes out her purse to pay Felix.

'How much must I pay you for that lovely chest?' she asks.

'May I have another slice of that delicious chocolate cake?' asks Felix.

'Of course,' says Mummy, and she gives Felix another big slice.

'So,' laughs Felix, 'it's paid for.'

'What do you mean?' asks Mummy. 'Is that all? One piece of cake?'

'Yes,' answers Felix, 'this delicious cake and your friendship more than repay me. Money doesn't make me that happy. But your friendship does.'

Mummy is speechless.

'Everywhere I go, doing odd jobs, I make new friends,' explains Felix. 'All those friends are more valuable to me than a chest filled with gold and diamonds. And you know what's nicest about that?' he asks the children.

John and Lisa shrug, saying nothing.

'Wherever I go, I get offered a delicious treat!' laughs Felix loudly. 'Enjoy your cake, children!' What a nice man Felix is!

LISA THE BOOKWORM

Daddy is working in his office. The office is filled with books. Thick and thin, big and little books. He really has a lot of them.

Lisa walks into the office.

'Daddy, could I borrow a really thick book from you?' she asks.

'Of course,' answers Daddy. 'Pick one out.'

Lisa picks out a thick book and walks out of the office. A bit later, she comes back.

'May I have another book?'

Daddy thinks it's nice that Lisa is suddenly so interested in books. 'Sure, go ahead,' he laughs.

'She will become a real bookworm, if she keeps on reading so much,' thinks Daddy as Lisa leaves the office.

Whoops – here's Lisa again. 'This time, may I borrow two books?'

'Go ahead,' laughs Daddy, surprised. 'I didn't know that you enjoyed books so much.'

Without a word Lisa leaves the room, with two

thick books tucked under her arm.

Daddy finds this a bit curious, and follows Lisa out of the room.

He sees her go into the kitchen.

He peers through the key-hole and watches Lisa.

She has pushed a chair over by the kitchen cabinet. On the chair lie two thick books. She puts the other two books on top of them. Then she climbs onto the chair and stands on the pile of books.

Lisa reaches up to the sweets jar that stands on the top shelf of the cabinet.

'What a clever girl. I thought that something wasn't right!' thinks Daddy. He tiptoes back to his office without a sound.

A little later Lisa brings the books back.

'So, Lisa,' asks Daddy, 'did you like the way the books tasted?'

Lisa turns red as a beetroot and runs out of the office....

PILLOWS

Lisa has a new bed.

She romps with John on the wonderful bed.

Don't they have to try it out?

They lay their heads back on the lovely new pillows.

'My, my, these pillows are soft,' says John. 'I want one of these.'

'Do you know what's inside a pillow?' asks Lisa. John thinks a moment. 'Feathers,' he answers, confidently.

'No, no,' Lisa teases him. 'I think there are little clouds inside. That's why they are so soft.'

John sits straight up. 'Not true,' he exclaims. 'There are feathers inside. Tiny, soft feathers!'

'No!' argues Lisa. 'There are tiny pink clouds inside!'

John gets mad and hits his sister with the pillow.

'Feathers!'

Lisa grabs the other pillow and swings it at John's head.

'Clouds!'

Boof! John attacks again. Lisa falls off the bed.

'FEATHERS!'

Lisa climbs back on the bed and gives John a clout with the pillow. He stands up, wobbling on his legs.

'CLOUDS!'

Then the pillow fight really breaks out. They give each other pretty hard hits with the pillows. Are they ever having fun!

Lisa swings so hard that she should knock John off the bed. But when the pillow hits John's back, it rips open.

Suddenly the room is filled with – feathers. They swirl like clouds of snow, and soon cover the whole room.

'See? I'm right!' laughs John, when a feather tickles his nose.

Will Mummy laugh too?

INVISIBLE LISA

Lisa is invisible. She is a secret agent on a dangerous mission. She has just cast a magic spell that makes her invisible. Now she can sneak around tracking bad guys.

Daddy sits in his office. Nosey lies near him, sound asleep. Lisa sneaks into the office.

'Hi, Lisa,' says Daddy.

'Shhh! You can't see me,' hisses Lisa. 'I'm invisible.'

'Oh, I didn't know that,' says Daddy.

He goes back to working as if nobody else is in the room.

Mummy is ironing in the living room. Lisa sneaks in.

'Lisa,' asks Mummy, 'will you please help me to fold these sheets?'

'I can't – I'm invisible!' hisses Lisa.

'Then I'll just ask your brother,' says Mummy, a little annoyed. Lisa slips out of the living room.

John is glad to help Mummy. They fold the sheets together.

'You've helped me quite a lot lately,' says Mummy to John. 'I think you have earned a sweet.'

They go together to the kitchen, where the sweets jar is.

John gets his sweet.

Just then Lisa wanders into the room. 'Do I get a sweet too?' she asks.

Mummy acts as if she doesn't see Lisa.

'Who asked that?'

'I did,' says Lisa. 'May I please have a sweet too?'

'But I can't see you,' teases Mummy.

'Oh yes you can,' protests Lisa, 'I'm not invisible any more. I've made myself visible! Do I get a sweet now?'

'John got a sweet because he had helped me,' answers Mummy. 'You didn't have time to help me. So you don't deserve a sweet.'

'Gee,' grumbles Lisa. 'It's always something.'

CHARADES

John and Lisa are playing charades with their parents.

They take turns acting something out without using words. The rest of the family has to guess what they are trying to be.

It's John's turn. He thinks hard.

'OK, I've got it,' he says.

John goes to the front of the room so everyone can see him. Then he stands stock still.

'A statue!' cries Lisa.

'A tree?' asks Mummy.

'A soldier who's guarding the king's palace,' tries Daddy.

'No,' says John, shaking his head.

He points at Mummy's yellow jumper and back at himself.

Everyone else is thinking hard.

'Are you yellow?' asks Daddy.

John nods.

'A yellow statue?' asks Mummy.

Next John looks at his sock. There's a hole in it. He stares at the hole.

'Is there a hole in you?' asks Lisa.

John nods and waves his hand.

'Are there many holes in you?' asks Mummy.

John nods harder.

'Let's see,' says Daddy. 'You don't move, you are yellow, and you have holes in you.'

'I know!' yells Lisa. 'A chunk of cheese!'

John narrows his eyes and waves his hands back and forth.

'We're close!' exclaims Daddy.

Then John turns around and bends over. He passes some gas.

It smells awful!

Everyone pinches their noses closed as fast as they can.

Suddenly Lisa has an inspiration.

'I know! Stinky cheese!!!'

John nods and everyone bursts out laughing.

John was a piece of stinky cheese!

HEFTY

Lisa and John are helping Daddy.

What are they up to?

They fill a big bucket with garden rubbish.

Mummy comes into the garden. She carries a big bowl of soup.

'This soup isn't good any more,' she says. 'Put it in too.' She pours it into the bucket.

'Look, Daddy,' says Lisa, 'here are some rotten potatoes.'

'That's great! Throw them in too,' answers Daddy.

It's becoming a horrible mess.

'Shall we throw in some grass?' laughs John.

Daddy stirs the stuff with a big stick.

'So, that's ready. It looks wonderful, doesn't it?' he asks.

John and Lisa nod.

Oh no, are they going to eat this awful stuff?

They load the bucket into a little red wagon.

Where are they going to take this mess?

John, Lisa and Daddy go down the hill.

Aha! The path leads them to Farmer Pete's farm.

Maybe this awful mess is for Farmer Pete?

No, that can't be. He wouldn't want that.

In a few minutes they come to the farm.

'Hello, Farmer Pete!' call the kids.

'Hello, everyone,' calls Farmer Pete back. 'She's over in the meadow.'

'Great, we'll find her,' answers Daddy.

They pull the wagon to the meadow.

In the middle of a mud puddle, they find a big cement trough. They dump the sloppy mixture into the trough.

A happy snuffling sound comes out of the barn.

A pink animal walks out.

'Happy Birthday, Hefty,' they all call to the animal.

Hefty begins to gobble up the mess. She thinks it's great.

Can you guess what kind of animal Hefty is?

DOORBELL JOKER

'Ding-dong,' sounds the doorbell.

'For heaven's sake,' cries Daddy. 'That is the fifth time already today! I'm getting fed up!'

Some joker rings and runs away fast as a rabbit. Daddy knows it's not John or Lisa, because they are sitting inside playing nicely with Nosey. Maybe they can help Daddy catch the bell-ringer?

John and Lisa are only too glad to help. They are slowly getting fed up with the noise of the bell too.

The children and Nosey run out and hide themselves behind a bush. They keep their eyes on the door.

It's not long before they spot someone creeping up to the door. He quickly rings the bell and runs away.

Aha! The children have seen who the rascal is.

They run to tell Daddy.

'Of course,' growls Daddy. 'Who else would it be besides that nuisance, Carl. We'll teach him a lesson. I have a little plan. Listen….'

A bit later Lisa is standing guard behind the bush. Nosey sits next to her. She doesn't have long to wait before Carl shows up again. He creeps cautiously toward the front door.

From her hiding place Lisa whistles to John, who's standing at the window.

'Now, Daddy!' yells John.

Just as Carl is about to ring the bell, the door swings open.

'Booo!' yells Daddy as loud as he can. Carl runs away screaming.

'We sure gave him a taste of his own medicine!' Daddy says, laughing.

Naming the Kittens

Today the children are going to visit the little kittens at Farmer Pete's.

They've already gotten bigger.

They still don't have names.

John and Lisa have already picked some: Topsie, Mopsie, Flopsie, and Hopsie.

The children will decide today which kitten gets which name. There are two striped and two black kittens.

Lisa lines the kittens up in a row.

'You are Topsie,' she says to one of the striped kittens.

She gives the black kitten next to Topsie the name of Mopsie. She names the other black kitten Flopsie, and the last striped kitten becomes Hopsie.

So that's done.

The kittens are already busy romping all around. They roll over each other. One bites another on the tail

while the third crawls over them both.

'Hey, Flopsie, you can't do that,' Lisa scolds a black kitten.

'Lisa, if you ask me, that's not Flopsie. This is Flopsie,' says John, showing her the other black kitten.

'No, that can't be. That is Mopsie,' laughs Lisa.

'No way!' answers John, 'that is Topsie! Topsie has stripes!'

'Not true, you dummy,' says Lisa angrily while she points to a black kitten. 'That is Flopsie and this is… No wait, that is Mopsie there.'

'That's because they are wrestling so much. This is Hopsie and this is… ah, this is…'

'See what I mean?' asks John, mad now. 'You don't even know yourself.'

After a pause, Lisa has to admit that she doesn't know any more.

But maybe you know?

SOUP

Lisa is helping Mummy make soup. Mummy has put a pile of vegetables on the table. They all have to be washed and cut into pieces.
There are carrots, leeks, a couple of onions, celery, tomatoes and two courgettes.
Lisa helps Mummy cut the vegetables up.
It takes a long time, but finally all of the vegetables are washed and cut. Mummy puts them into the soup pot.
She turns the heat on and lets the vegetables start to cook. Then she adds some water.
'If you like, you can make some little meatballs for the soup,' Mummy suggests.
'Sure! That would be fun,' says Lisa.
Mummy gives Lisa a package of ground meat. Lisa takes a little of it and rolls it between her hands until it becomes a nice ball. Then she lays the ball on a plate.

Meanwhile Mummy has gone to the laundry. Lisa leaves the plate with the meatballs on the table. She wants to ask Mummy if it's time to put them in the soup.
But what happens? When she comes back to the kitchen, all the meatballs are gone! Where could they be?
A strange sound comes from under the table. Mummy lifts up the tablecloth and she sees Nosey. He's just finishing the last meatball.
Mummy gets angry at Nosey. He realizes that he's done something naughty. He hangs his head and looks guiltily at the floor.
For his punishment, he must go and sit in his basket.

Later on, Mummy and Lisa taste the soup. It tastes delicious! Even without meatballs....

TINY ELF AT THE LIBRARY

Lisa and John are going to the library with Mummy.

What Mummy doesn't know is that Lisa has an elf in her pocket.

It is Tiny Elf. He wanted to go along to the library. Like all elves, he loves to read an exciting book. But he can't borrow a book himself.

The librarian would scream her head off. An elf borrowing a book! Just imagine….

So Lisa is going to act as if she's borrowing one for herself.

'Do you think this is a nice book?' asks Lisa. From out of her jacket pocket, the elf looks at the book. *The Girl Who Was in Love* is the name of the book.

'Bah! No!' whispers the elf gruffly. 'I want something exciting!'

'This one, then? This looks exciting to me,' says Lisa.

'*The Sport Contest?* No! I want ghosts and monsters with sharp teeth and long nails!'

Tiny Elf starts to act crazy inside Lisa's pocket, as if he's become a monster himself.

'Calm down and be quiet,' whispers Lisa warningly. 'Soon somebody will see you! What do you think of this title: *The Vampire Castle?*'

On the cover of the book there's a scary castle. Bats with red eyes fly around it.

'Yesss! That's what I want to read!'

Lisa brings the book to the counter. Mummy

and John stand nearby, watching.

'What a strange book you have chosen,' says Mummy. 'If you get nightmares from it, we are bringing it right back, dear.'

'Nightmares? Me?' protests Lisa. But to herself, she thinks, 'Ugh, what an awful book. I would NEVER want to read that one….'

GHOSTS

In his house, Tiny Elf is completely lost in his scary book.

The book is full of vampires, ghosts and monsters. The story is terribly exciting. Suddenly the elf hears a commotion. He puts his book down and opens the door cautiously. In the half-dark he sees something moving. It looks like white sheets. It's…GHOSTS!

Tiny Elf trembles with fear. He quickly slams the door shut.

'Wooooooooo!' moan the ghosts with spooky, deep voices.

Then it gets quiet again.

'It…it's just my imagination. Oh, I've read too much of my book, I think. And now my fantasies are coming true.'

It's quiet for a while.

Tiny Elf feels better and sighs with relief. 'See? It was my imagination.'

But then suddenly he hears a loud 'WOOOOO!' The ghosts are right outside the elf's house!

'Wooooooooo,' moan the ghosts again.

'Oh no!' yells Tiny Elf, terrified. 'I'm not reading any more scary books!'

Then he hears giggles outside his door.

Hey, those voices. That's…

'Hello,' he hears.

It's John and Lisa.

'Have we scared you?' they laugh.

'Scared? Who, me?' growls the elf bravely. 'An elf is never scared! I was just acting. Now leave me alone. I want to read my book some more.'

As soon as the children are gone, the elf starts doing his chores. He's never going to read any more of that scary book!

BLIND MAN'S BLUFF

'Shall we play Blind Man's Bluff?' asks John's teacher.

The children think that's a great idea.

John plays the blind man. The teacher ties a blindfold over his eyes. Then she spins John around and the game begins. John walks with tiny steps, his arms out in front of him.

The children run around John. He wiggles his fingers, ready to grab them, but he doesn't catch anyone.

All around him, John hears the children calling to him. But they are too fast for him to catch.

Steve, John's best friend, calls his name. John walks in the direction of his voice. Yes! He's caught Steve.

'I gotcha! Now you're the blind man,' exclaims John.

'That's not fair,' protests Steve. 'You peeked.'

'That's not true,' cries John, surprised.

'Is too,' exclaims

Steve angrily.

The teacher steps between the two.

'What's going on here? Did you peek, John?' she asks.

John shakes his head. 'You liar!' cries Steve.

'Not true!' yells John.

'Hold on here, you two,' the teacher interrupts the two noisemakers.

'One of you is lying, and I think that's awful. I want to know which one of you is lying. Otherwise both of you will have to stand in the corner for five minutes.'

The boys look at each other angrily.

'I've lied…,' admits Steve after a pause.

The teacher sits by Steve.

'It was not nice to tell a lie about your best friend,' she says, 'but because you were so honest and admitted it, I'm not going to punish you.'

Soon the children are back to playing the game. And John and Steve are back to being best friends.

COUNTING SHEEP

Lisa can't fall asleep. She has already been in bed a long time.

She turns onto her tummy. A little later she turns to her back with a sigh. Still later she rolls up in a ball. Then after a while she lies with her arms and legs stretched out.

Each time she tosses and turns, she wakes up completely.

Then she gets an idea.

'I'm going to count sheep,' she thinks.

She imagines a white fence and a green meadow. Whoops! The first sheep jumps over the

fence.

'One,' she counts in her mind.

Then comes number two. Here is number three….

She goes on like this until she's counted nearly fifty sheep. Lisa is still awake.

'Just count further,' she thinks.

Fifty-one, fifty-two, fifty….

What is that?

That's no white sheep. No, it's an orange sheep.

The next sheep jumps over the fence.

Go on…this sheep has sunglasses on.

Then comes one with a jumper on! And that one there jumps with a pogo stick.

Lisa is curious to see what the next sheep will look like.

She doesn't see any more sheep, but she does see a little boy. It's John, scrambling over the fence. After John comes Nosey.

Now everything is crazy! Mummy and Daddy jump over the fence. They still have their pyjamas on. Daddy has a clown nose on. They call out to Lisa.

'Lisa! Lisa! Hello…it's time to get up. You need to go to school!'

Lisa blinks her eyes….

Slowly it comes back to her. What a strange dream!

VALENTINES

Today the teacher has an arts and crafts project for the children.

They each get a piece of paper which has a heart drawn on it. They have to fill it in with beautiful colours and then cut it out.

When that's done, the teacher glues the heart on a stick.

'You can give your heart to someone that you think is nice, because today is Valentine's Day. That is the day for people in love.'

The children get busy right away.

John colours in his heart beautifully. Then he takes a scissors and cuts the heart out. He finds this much harder than colouring.

Soon the heart is cut out.

John takes it to the teacher. She pastes it on a stick and writes John's name on it.

'It's all done!' she says. 'Do you already know who you'll give it to?'

John nods.

John likes Annie, a girl in his class. They like to play together. Sometimes they sit together on the bench during recess. They eat their snacks together. One day Annie's mother forgot to give her something to eat. John gave her his biscuit. Annie was very happy about that.

'But then you didn't have any biscuits for yourself?' asks John's teacher.

Yes, but John didn't really mind that too much.

All the children run to the playground with their paper hearts in their hands.

John looks for Annie.

There she is.

'Hello,' says John.

With a shy smile John gives his heart to Annie.

Do you know what? Annie smiles back. She's also made a heart. And she gives it to John....

49

NOSEY RUNS AWAY

Oh boy. Nosey has run away.

John and Lisa have looked all over for him. Nosey is nowhere to be found.

Mummy and Daddy have looked for him too. They have even been over to Farmer Pete's. He hasn't seen Nosey. They have looked in the woods and fields. Nosey is nowhere to be found.

Maybe he's been kidnapped? Or has he had an accident?

Everybody is worried about Nosey.

'Come,' says Daddy, comfortingly. 'Let's go home. Who knows, maybe Nosey is already standing by the door, barking to be let in.'

They hurry home.

Nosey isn't there....

A bit later the children sit silently looking out the window. Outside it's already getting a little darker. Poor Nosey, where are you?

Then the phone rings.

Daddy answers it. It is the butcher.

'There's been a little dog here in my shop all afternoon. He looks a lot like your dog. If he's yours, come get him quickly, because he's eaten up nearly all of my sausages.'

'We'll be there right away to pick him up,' says Daddy.

But of course! Why hadn't they thought of that? Every time they go to the butcher, he gives Nosey a little piece of sausage. The dog is crazy about sausage.

That's why he's gone to the butcher's all by himself. He really wanted a treat.

'Come on, put your jackets on. We're going to get Nosey,' says Daddy to the children. He doesn't need to say it twice. John and Lisa storm out the door.

A little later Nosey is back home. With a bulging tummy, he crawls into his basket and falls fast asleep. Will he dream of still more sausages?

50

SHRUNKEN CLOTHING

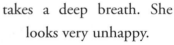

'Oh no!' cries Mummy. She is in the laundry. Lisa runs to her mother. 'What's happened, Mummy?' Lisa asks, worried.

'Goodness gracious! Men don't know anything about washing clothes!'

Lisa looks at her mother, puzzled. 'I asked Daddy to load the washing machine before he left. But he set the temperature of the water too high, and now all the clothes have shrunken.'

Mummy pulls a jumper out of the machine and holds it up to her chest. The jumper is half as big as it used to be.

'I can't wear this any more. My beautiful jumper…,' she wails.

She pulls a skirt out of the washing machine.

'Oh no, this skirt is also ruined…and I liked it so much!'

Mummy sits down on the floor hopelessly and takes a deep breath. She looks very unhappy.

'All those nice clothes… now they're the size of doll clothes….'

A little bell goes off in Lisa's mind. Hmmm. Doll clothes?

'Um, Mummy?' she asks hesitatingly. 'May I have the clothes?'

'Oh, go ahead and take them,' sighs Mummy. 'I can't wear them.'

Then they hear the clinking of keys. The front door opens.

'I'm home!' calls Daddy happily.

Mummy stands up and pushes up her sleeves. She stomps toward Daddy.

Lisa meanwhile grabs as many clothes as she can and takes them to her room.

While Daddy and Mummy talk things over, Lisa plays with her dolls. They have just gotten a lovely stylish wardrobe.

THE DETECTIVE

Lisa and John have been to Mrs Holly's shop for their mother. Lisa carries the shopping bag. On the way home they come upon Carl. He's wearing a funny hat and a long rain jacket. In his hand he holds a magnifying glass.

'Boy, do you look silly,' says Lisa.

'I'm a detective,' says Carl. 'Not just a detective. No, I'm the best! Carl the Superdetective! I know everything about everyone. So I know that you've been to the shop and you've bought a box of biscuits.'

Even Lisa and John are impressed.

How could Carl know that?

But then it dawns on Lisa. She looks down at the shopping bag. Naturally, Carl has seen the bag. The box of biscuits sticks out a little. That explains how he knows they have bought biscuits.

'Boy, what a fake,' says Lisa. 'I can see that too.' Carl narrows his eyes in anger.

'Oh yeah?' he snarls. 'Then tell me something I don't know yet.'

Lisa looks Carl over from head to foot. Then a broad smile covers her face.

'So what do YOU know, huh?' he says, just to tease her.

'Well, I know that as soon as you go inside, you'll come back out really fast....'

'Why would that be?' Carl wants to know.

'Because you've stepped in dog poop, that's why!' bursts out Lisa.

Carl looks at his messy shoe and makes a face. He dashes away.

Lisa and John have to admit one thing about Carl: he's the fastest detective they have ever seen.

53

CRAZY SAM

Mummy and Daddy are going out tonight. That's why Samantha is coming. She's a babysitter and she's coming for the first time. She says, 'You can call me Sam for short.'

After Mummy and Daddy have left, Sam asks, 'What shall we do?'

'Do we have to go to bed now?' asks Lisa.

'Are you crazy? We have to do our treasure hunt!'

The children don't understand her.

'Just follow me,' says Sam.

Sam climbs up on the table. 'Quick, come on up. The airplane is about to take off!'

John and Lisa climb on top of the table.

'We are flying over the jungle. Grab your parachute. We're going to jump.'

Sam jumps off the table. The children follow her. They act as if they are floating down.

'Help,' yells Sam, 'I'm stuck in a tree! A giant snake wants to eat me up!'

The children hurry to help Sam. She cuts the head of the snake off. Chop!

'Ooof, that was close,' sighs Sam. 'We have to escape from this jungle. Lisa, have you brought a map?'

'Of course,' says Lisa confidently.

'John, can you make sure that no monsters get us?'

'Bam, bam!' With his zap gun, John shoots all the monsters.

They run and creep, dive and slide through the house until Sam says, 'Shhh, there it is. The last thing we have to do is jump over this river full of crocodiles. Are you ready?' John and Lisa nod.

'Jump!' yells Sam. The three jump over the river. They land with a thump in bed.

'So,' says Sam. 'Now you need to rest a bit.'

John and Lisa nod. They are pretty tired.

'Sleep well,' whispers crazy Sam as she tucks them in. What a night!

NOSEY IS SICK

Mummy has called the vet, because Nosey is sick.

He lies all day long in his basket, looking sad. The children find it very strange.

Nosey always wants to run and play with John and Lisa. But not today. He lies with his head between his paws and looks around quietly.

John and Lisa sit beside Nosey. Lisa has put one of her dolly's blankets over him. At least that way he'll be nice and warm.

'I hope he doesn't die...,' says John.

'That would be awful,' says Lisa sadly.

Here comes the vet.

He sits down by the children and looks carefully at Nosey. He shines a light in Nosey's eyes.

Then he looks at Nosey's throat.

'Is he going to die?' asks John with a trembling voice.

'Absolutely not,' says the vet. 'He just has an ordinary cold. I'll give him some medicine. He'll feel much better tomorrow.'

John and Lisa cheer up immediately.

The vet takes a needle out of his bag.

John and Lisa don't like the pointy needle at all.

Nosey jumps a little when the vet gives him his injection. Then he puts his head down and sleeps.

The next morning, John wakes up to the sound of paws padding into his room.

He jumps quickly out of bed. 'Nosey, you're all better again!' he cries.

Lisa comes to see.

'Nosey, dear sweet Nosey,' she croons. The children hug Nosey as hard as they can.

A little later all three of them go to the garden and play all day.

They are so happy that Nosey is well again!

MAN ON THE MOON

The children are going to visit their grannie and grandad.

Grandad has bought a telescope. It is a big one, and it stands on its own feet.

'This way I can really see the stars and moon,' says Grandad.

John looks first through the long tube.

'Wow! I see a pancake!' he cries, surprised. 'A giant pancake!'

'Ha-ha-ha-ha-ha,' laughs Grandad, 'that's not a pancake. That's the moon.'

'I didn't know the moon was so big,' says John, amazed.

'Hey!' says John, 'There's a man walking on the moon....'

'Can I look?' asks Lisa.

John steps back so Lisa can look too.

She peers carefully through the telescope.

'Hey, yeah!' she yells, surprised. 'There's a man walking on the moon! A little green man, Grandad!'

'Do you think I'm crazy?' asks Grandad.

'See for yourself,' says Lisa.

Grandad bends over the telescope.

'I'm looking, but I don't see any little green men,' says Grandad.

'How can that be?' asks Lisa. 'Let me take a look again.'

Grandad steps aside so Lisa can look.

'I see him! Really! There he is again!' cries Lisa excitedly.

Grandad quickly looks through the telescope.

'I still don't see him,' he grumbles.

'Are you trying to make fun of me, you two little rascals?'

Lisa and John take turns looking through the telescope.

This time they don't see anything. The little man is gone, they say.

Have they played a trick on Grandad? Or have they really seen a man on the moon?

Who can tell?

56

DIET

Daddy is too fat. He can't button his trousers any more.

'Then you'll have to go on a diet,' laughs Mummy.

Daddy looks at her with surprise.

'Oh, no, no diet for me,' he protests.

Whenever they sit down for dinner, Daddy gets a tiny little serving of rice.

Mummy and the children eat chicken and chips.

Grumbling, Daddy eats his rice.

As a treat, the children get some ice cream. Daddy gets none.

Daddy looks longingly at the children's ice cream.

'No,' says Mummy when she sees Daddy.

'It won't work. You're not getting any, no matter what you do.'

Mummy begins to clear the table.

When Mummy isn't looking, he leans over to Lisa.

'May I please have a little?' he whispers.

'No,' says Lisa loudly, so that Mummy can hear.

Mummy turns around quickly.

Daddy tries to look as if nothing has happened.

'If you do that one more time…,' says Mummy sternly to Daddy.

'This dumb diet,' whinges Daddy.

'You're too fat. You're bursting out of your trousers.'

'That's not true!' he cries.

'Yes it is – you are too fat,' answers Mummy.

Now Daddy is really angry.

'I AM NOT TOO FAT!' he roars. His fat tummy shakes.

'Boing!' a button pops off Daddy's trousers. Oh no – his trousers are going to fall down.

Mummy and the children burst out laughing.

Grumbling, Daddy hitches up his trousers.

He will stay on his diet.

COLD AND HOT

Farmer Pete has brought a whole load of old logs for the fireplace. They need to be cut in small pieces as soon as possible, he says, before it starts to rain. Because when wood is wet, it doesn't burn well.

Today it's cold and windy. The wind feels so cold that it freezes your cheeks.

Daddy puts on his warm clothes. Lisa and John put on thick, warm clothing too, because they can help Daddy.

Daddy saws the big logs in smaller chunks. He chops the chunks in still smaller pieces with an axe. John and Lisa can carry the pieces to the garden shed.

After several hours of hard work, all the logs are cut into smaller pieces. In the garden shed there's a whole pile of them.

'Shall we light a fire?' asks Daddy.

The children are totally frozen. A warm fire in the fireplace sounds like a great idea.

When they go inside, Daddy brings along some wood.

John and Lisa are still shivering from the cold as they stand in front of the fire.

The flames drive the cold out of their bodies bit by bit.

Mummy brings everyone a delicious cup of steaming hot chocolate.

'This will fix you up,' she says. The children carefully taste the chocolate. It's wonderful.

It feels like the hot chocolate has even gone down to their toes.

In a short while the room gets nice and warm.

So warm that they get sleepy.

So sleepy that they… fall… asleep.

WINTER CAMP

Lisa and John have found a tent in the garage. 'May we camp in the garden?' they ask Daddy, who is hard at work in his office.

Daddy laughs. 'It's raining and it's freezing cold. It's best you stay indoors.'

Disappointed, the children drift away.

They wanted so much to go camping. What a shame.

Then Lisa has an idea.

'What if we camp inside?'

'Oh yeah,' cries John, thrilled. 'That's a great idea.'

The pair of them drag the big sack with the tent in it into the living room. They pull the tent out.

'Do you know how this goes together?' asks John while he pulls out stakes and ropes.

Lisa, who has crept under the tent, doesn't know.

A little later they have a solution. They lay the tent over a few chairs, fasten it with clothes pegs, and the tent is ready. Not exactly as it is supposed to be, but it's cosy inside.

What do they need now?

Sleeping bags, a cooking kit, and all sorts of stuff. Lisa and John rummage through the whole house, looking for what they need.

After a while they have everything ready at their tent. They have filled a little dish with chocolate biscuits.

'Food's ready,' says Lisa.

They lie side by side, cosy in their warm sleeping bags.

They eat the biscuits and look at the nasty weather outdoors. The rain splatters against the window.

'Nothing is as nice as camping indoors,' sighs Lisa, lazily.

'Mmm,' answers John, and he bites into his biscuit.

DARKNESS

'Mummy, where are my skates? My class is going skating tomorrow.'

'They are in the garden shed,' answers Mummy. 'You'll have to go and get them.'

'But it's dark outside…,' says Lisa.

'Are you afraid of the dark?' teases Mummy.

'No way,' says Lisa. 'I'm on my way.'

'I'll put on the outdoor light for you anyway,' says Mummy.

A moment later Lisa is outside, all alone.

The yard light shines on the bushes at the front of the garden. Behind them she sees nothing but scary shadows.

Lisa swallows and walks to the garden shed.

In daylight the shed isn't far away, but in the pitch black darkness it seems twice as far.

Oooh! Something is moving over there!

Lisa listens, then sighs. It's only a bush that's waving back and forth in the wind.

What was that? A pair of yellow eyes!

Lisa freezes.

'Meow.' It's Sparkle, Farmer Pete's cat. She's hunting mice.

Lisa takes tiny steps forward in the darkness.

Finally. There's the garden shed.

Lisa opens the door and turns the light on. It's quiet. She wants to get out of here fast. She grabs her skates. Then Lisa runs outside, into the darkness.

'Yoo-hoo-hoo-hoo!' sounds suddenly behind her.

Lisa's hair stands on end. In panic, she runs up the path as fast as she can. A dark shadow with flapping wings follows her.

Lisa storms into the house and slams the door shut. Her heart pounds in her chest.

If she ever needs anything else from the garden shed, she will wait until it's light out….

NO MORE STABILISERS

Daddy has taken the stabilisers off John's bike. Now John must learn to ride his bike like the big kids. With two wheels. Not at all easy!

John gets on his bike. He's just a little scared. He pushes the pedals. Slowly the bike wobbles and moves. Daddy holds tight to John's arm.

Bit by bit they go faster. Daddy has to run a little to keep up.

Then Daddy lets John loose. To John, it seems like the bike will crash. Luckily, Daddy grabs him again quickly.

'Keep pedalling,' he says. 'You're doing great.'

John pedals hard. Now and then Daddy lets go of him. It's going better and better.

Suddenly John is riding along all by himself.

'Yesss!' yells Daddy happily. 'You're doing it!'

Then something goes wrong. The bike swerves dangerously left and right. Boom! John lies on the street, crying.

Daddy comes to him to pick him up. He wipes away John's tears with his handkerchief.

John doesn't want to cycle any more.

'Come on, little tiger,' says Daddy. 'You almost did it. Are you going to give up just because you fell once? You know what? As soon as you can ride a bike, we can ride together to Mrs Holly's shop. Then I'll get you a lollipop.'

Not long after that, a big bike stands in front of Mrs Holly's shop. Next to it stands a little bike. Without stabilisers.

DREAM BOOK

Tiny Elf has a fat book.

He got it from his father.

And he got it from his father, Tiny Elf's grandfather. And his grandfather got it from his father. And Tiny Elf forgets who gave it to him.

It's a really special book. It's very thick and has a gold covering wrapped around it. The pages are so old that they are a little yellow.

The elves call it *The Dream Book.* Whenever elves have a beautiful dream, they write it in the book.

There are lots of dreams in the thick book.

Sweet dreams that smell like fresh baked bread.

Lovely dreams that make you think about white summer clouds. Funny dreams that tickle your toes. Colourful dreams that remind you of a summer field with the most beautiful flowers. Romantic dreams that you hug and that make your head light up….

Nasty dreams can't be in the book. No, the elves forget them as fast as possible.

And do you know what the elves love to do?

First they take a warm bath, and they soak there a long time. Then they jump into their favourite pyjamas and go to bed. Then they sniff the fresh sheets, which smell like lavender and thyme.

After that they read a dream or two from the dream book. And then, with their heads full of lovely dreams, they fall fast asleep.

When the morning breaks, there's a new dream ready for the book.

What shall it be about this time?

DOCTOR JOHN

Today John is a doctor. He's so busy!

He runs through the house with his doctor kit.

He's just been called. A child has fallen on the stairs.

When he comes to the stairs, he sees the poor victim. It's a cloth doll, with its legs all in a knot.

'We'll take a look,' says the doctor seriously. He picks up one of the doll's legs. 'Oh dear,' he says seriously, 'that needs to be bandaged.'

He pulls a roll of bandage out of his doctor's kit and wraps up one leg of the doll. But the doll's leg is short, and there is still a lot of bandage left over.

John takes a big scissors out of his doctor's kit. The scissors belong to Mummy. He's taken them because they cut so well.

John wants to use the scissors to cut the bandage. He holds them in one hand, while he holds the bandage in the other.

The scissors snap shut. 'Ow!' yells John.

He's cut his own finger! It's bleeding.

John cries.

Mummy comes to see what's going on.

When she sees the scissors, she knows immediately what has happened.

She picks John up quickly, to look at the wound. It's good that it isn't a big cut. She puts a plaster decorated with little animals on the cut.

'You must not use these,' she says angrily, waving the scissors. 'Just see what happens.'

Embarrassed, John nods and promises that he will never do that again.

Then he runs off.

Doctors are so busy....

COMPUTER

'Do you know what I just saw?' asks Mummy as soon as she comes home.

'I was driving in the town, doing some errands. I parked the car in a free spot by the park. When I got out, I saw an old man with thick glasses on his nose in the park. He seemed friendly and he stood there, looking around. Suddenly he cried, "Computer!"

'"What a strange fellow," I thought.

'I looked around, but didn't give it any more thought. I opened the boot of my car and grabbed my shopping bag. When I closed the boot again, I saw the man was still standing there. Once again he yelled, "Computer!"

'"What a strange fellow," I thought again.

"Why is he standing there yelling?"

'The man looked anxiously around the park. He was surely looking for something. He looked to the left, then the right.

'His voice rang through the park: "Computer! Computer!" He seemed like a crazy parrot.

'I decided to investigate. Maybe the man was a bit confused and needed some help?

'I walked up to the old man cautiously.

'He stood there peering through his thick glasses. I just wanted to ask if I could help him, when I heard a dog barking.

'"Ah, there you are!" cried the old man to the dog, who came up to him. "Come, Pewter, let's go home...."'

CIRCUS DOG

Lisa is watching a show about circuses on telly with Nosey. They watch acrobats who do dangerous tricks on the flying trapeze. Now a clown steps into the ring with his dog. The dog looks like Nosey.

Whenever Nosey sees the dog, he perks up his ears and watches carefully. 'Maybe that's Nosey's brother,' thinks Lisa.

The clown has the dog do some tricks.

First the dog dances on his hind legs.

Nosey barks and tries to stand on his hind legs.

'Maybe Nosey wants to be a circus dog?' thinks Lisa.

The clown throws plastic rings to the dog. The dog catches the rings in his mouth and doesn't drop a single one. Bravo!

Lisa claps her hands and

Nosey barks as loud as he can and wags his tail.

Nosey grabs his ring toy and tosses it in the air. He catches it in his mouth.

'What fun! He's doing the same tricks,' thinks Lisa.

Nosey watches the dog on the television, his tongue hanging out.

The clown takes a big hoop and shows it to the audience. The drums roll.

The clown hangs the hoop on a hook.

With a torch, he sets the hoop on fire.

The drums roll louder.

Lisa and Nosey watch, fascinated. With a big jump, the dog leaps through the burning hoop.

Nosey sits as still as a statue and begins to pant.

That's one trick that Nosey won't try!

You have to be a circus dog to do that.

TASTING THINGS

Dinner is ready.

While the children come to sit at the table, chattering happily, they ask Mummy what she's made.

'Brussels sprouts,' says Mummy evenly.

All at once the children's good humour disappears.

'I don't want any,' says Lisa. She crosses her arms over her chest and looks straight ahead crossly.

'Me either,' grumbles John.

'But you have to taste them,' says Daddy firmly. 'Mummy has made a nice mustard sauce to go with them.'

'Come on,' urges Mummy. 'I got the recipe from a friend of mine. Her children didn't like to eat sprouts before, but now they love them.'

The children give Mummy dark looks.

Meanwhile Daddy has put two Brussels sprouts on each plate.

'Each of you must try a bit,' he says. 'Then you can honestly say whether you like them or not. But you must try them first.'

It takes a while, but finally both John and Lisa try the sprouts.

They slowly, slowly chew their vegetables.

'And?' asks Mummy curiously.

First the children look mean. Then smiles slide over their faces.

'You like them after all, don't you, huh?' laughs Mummy.

'I think it's great that you both tried them,' says Daddy. 'Just remember that. You must always try a little bit.'

The children eat their sprouts up. They ask for more. After a while Mummy says there's also a dessert.

'Ice cream!' cry the children.

'Yes! Sprout ice cream!' teases Daddy.

'Mmm, yummy!' laugh the children.

MUMMY HAS A BIRTHDAY

John, Lisa and Daddy are up early, because today is Mummy's birthday.

They've thought up a nice surprise for her. Was it ever hard to keep it a secret!

Finally that's over.

John, Lisa and Daddy sneak down the stairs as quietly as they can. They tiptoe into the kitchen.

'Let's get to work, children,' says Daddy.

Daddy pops some rolls in the oven, makes tea, and cooks an egg. Lisa squeezes an orange and pours the juice into a glass. John spoons some jam into a little dish.

When everything is ready, Daddy puts everything on a tray. The fresh rolls and tea smell wonderful.

Lisa picks up a colourful birthday crown from the toy chest. She's worked on it a long time.

Won't Mummy be happy!

Everything is ready now. Quietly the three of them go up the stairs.

Mummy is still asleep.

'Happy Birthday to you!' they sing.

Mummy wakes up, smiles, and sits up in bed.

Daddy sets the tray on her lap.

'Breakfast in bed for the birthday girl,' he laughs, and gives Mummy a big kiss.

John sets the crown on Mummy's head.

'What a beautiful crown,' she says.

'This is a really nice present.'

'We have another present, too,' laugh the children.

'You do?' asks Mummy.

'We are going to the zoo!' says Lisa excitedly.

'Oh, that's great!' cries Mummy.

'Yes, but first you have to have your breakfast,' smiles John, 'and then we can go.'

DEAR DIARY

Dear Diary,

Since it was Mummy's birthday yesterday, we went to the zoo.

We saw lots of animals there.

I think the best one was the koala bear. It's a cute, cuddly, sleepy little animal that lives in trees.

Daddy says that they are very fussy eaters. They only will eat the leaves from one kind of tree, which has a hard name. If I don't eat everything Mummy cooks for me, I get punished.

I thought the giraffes were also pretty.

Only I wouldn't want to have such a long neck. I would have to duck my head every time I came inside. Luckily the giraffes have a very high cage.

The monkeys were fun. They are just like clowns in a circus. Mummy says that sometimes we are like monkeys too. Is that because we like bananas?

We saw some flamingos too. They stand on one foot. That's silly, really, because they have two. Wouldn't they fall down sometimes?

We laughed so much at the elephants! They can really make trouble with their long trunks. Behind us stood a big man wearing a hat. Suddenly the elephant grabbed his hat and threw it far away. The big man didn't think that was funny at all. We did.

I was a little scared of the lion. Especially when the father lion began to roar loudly. Daddy says that lions are in the same family as Sparkle, the cat. I say that's not true, because lions don't say meow. Daddy says I make bad jokes. After the zoo we went to have ice cream. Birthdays are the nicest days of the year.

THE POWER GOES OFF

A strong wind is blowing and big hailstones are clattering on the ground. Big, dark clouds fill the sky. It's really not a good day to play outside.

John and Lisa sit at the table, watching a film.

Mummy is ironing. It's so dark outside, she's turned on the lamps.

Daddy is working on his computer in his office.

Suddenly there's a flash of lightning, followed by a huge clap of thunder.

Then it's dark in the house.

Nothing works any more. Not the telly, not the lights, not the iron, and not the computer.

Mummy quickly lights some candles. Where have John and Lisa gone?

Mummy sees something moving under the table. Lisa peers out cautiously with fear in her eyes. Then

Mummy sees John under there too. She goes over to the children and holds them close to her.

It's suddenly got strangely quiet in the house. Apart from the clatter of the hailstones against the roof there is nothing to be heard.

'Don't be afraid,' says Mummy calmly. 'The lightning has turned off the power. It will come back in a second. Everything will be fine.' She smiles.

In a moment the lights come back on.

Relieved, the children take a deep breath.

There's another clap of thunder, but this one is not so loud.

The lights stay on. John and Lisa stay sitting close to Mummy.

It's warm there.

And safe.

MEGAN

teacher begins to speak.

'In a moment we're going to get to meet our new classmate. I can see you're already very curious. She has asked me to tell you about her first.'

The children look at each other in wonder.

'Megan – that's her name – had a bad accident last year. It hurt her legs very badly. Megan uses a wheelchair now.'

Silence falls over the class.

The teacher opens the classroom door and smiles.

'Come on in, Megan.'

Megan rolls her wheelchair into the classroom. It's decorated with coloured stickers and has bright red wheels.

'Hello, everyone,' says Megan cheerfully.

'Hello, Megan,' say all the children back.

'You can sit at this desk,' says the teacher.

'Is it okay with you that I brought my own chair?' Megan asks the teacher.

'Your own chair?'

'Yes, my wheelchair!' says Megan playfully.

The children burst out laughing. It's going to be fun to have Megan in the class!

Today a new girl is going to join Lisa's class.

At the playground, everyone is excited about it. They peer around, looking for a new face. But they don't see anyone they haven't seen before. When the bell rings, all the children go and stand in a line.

Maybe the newcomer is already waiting in the classroom. No, she isn't there either.

There's a desk ready for her. But no chair.

Has the teacher forgotten something?

When all the children are in their seats, the

SPORTS DAY

Today it's Sports Day. John has his new blue track suit on.

That way he'll play better.

The teachers have gotten all kinds of equipment ready in the gym.

When the children go into the gym, there is lots of excited shouting. They want to get started.

'A little less noise, please, boys,' says the teacher. 'You'll get to try everything.'

First they all run to the balancing beam.

John gets to be the first to try to walk from one end to the other, wearing a big hat. You can't let the hat fall to the floor.

Yippee! He actually did it!

Then the children go through an obstacle course. As fast as he can, John zigzags between the posts, crawls under a chair, and jumps from the bench. The teacher says John did very well.

Next they have to throw a ball into a basket. The basket is on a stool.

Was that ever hard!

The balls bounce all over the gym.

The teacher sets up a pair of hoops.

The children have to crawl through the hoops without touching them. That is not easy, because the hoops fall at the slightest touch. John is very careful and doesn't touch them at all. What a star!

'Now we're going to do scarf-dancing!' says the teacher.

Each child gets a long, silky scarf. The teacher teaches them how to dance, waving their scarves. All the children try to do their best and wave the scarves around. It looks beautiful.

They play the whole day. Super-fun!

When John gets home that afternoon he's really, really tired.

He falls on the sofa, exhausted.

'Sports Day is really great,' he sighs, 'but really tiring!'

ELF IN LOVE

'You came when I called. Thanks,' says Tiny Elf.

'What can I do to help?' asks Lisa, curious.

Tiny Elf goes into his little house. A moment later he comes back with a photo. It's an old black and white photo. It shows a young lady. She has a sparkling smile and is very pretty.

'Look,' says Tiny Elf, 'I think this is the most beautiful girl in the world.' He gives the lady a loud kiss on her paper mouth.

'I found her photo in an old box. Since then I can think of nothing but her.'

'Are you in love with her?' Lisa wants to know.

'Head over heels,' says the elf dreamily. 'Sadly, I don't know this beautiful angel's name or

where she lives. So I wanted to ask you if maybe you can tell me, so I can write her a letter.'

'May I look?' asks Lisa.

Lisa holds the picture carefully and looks at it closely.

Yes, she's seen that face before. But where? Suddenly she knows.

'I think I have bad news for you, little friend. That young lady has become an older lady. She's been married a long time and already has grandchildren. Do you know who this is?'

Disappointed, Tiny Elf shakes his head.

'She's a queen,' laughs Lisa. 'You're in love with a queen.'

The poor little guy.

'Oh well,' he sighs, 'even though she's older and married now, I can still write her a letter, can't I?'

LETTER TO THE QUEEN

'Click, click, click,' go the heels of the footman as he walks through the halls of the palace. The footman carries an envelope on a silver tray.
On it, in teeny little letters, is written, "Letter to the Queen.'
The footman knocks on a gilded door.
'Come in,' he hears.
'You have some mail, your Majesty,' he says.
The queen takes the letter from the silver tray.

'What a charming letter,' she says, in wonder. She carefully opens the letter and peers at the tiny handwriting.
'I'm afraid I need a magnifying glass.'
'I'll get one, your Majesty.'
'Tap, tap, tap.' The footman runs through the halls of the palace to get the magnifying glass.
'That is one problem when you live in a big palace,' sighs the Queen. 'You always have to go so far when you need something.'
A bit later the footman brings the magnifying glass. Now the Queen begins to read.

Dearest Queen of My Dreams,
I am only a tiny elf. But even though I'm small, I love you with my whole heart, as if I were a giant. Thus I want to ask you, lady of my dreams: Will you marry me?
Sincerely yours,
Tiny Elf

The Queen gets a warm feeling all over.
'Yes, of course I will marry you, my darling elf,' she cries excitedly.
'Oh, my angel,' cries Tiny Elf, as he jumps up in front of the Queen's nose.
Then a bell rings.
Riiiiinnnnnnggggg!
It's Tiny Elf's alarm clock.
It was all just a dream.

DADDIES DON'T PLAY

'Daddy, will you play building blocks with us?' John asks Daddy.

'Daddies don't play with blocks,' he laughs.

'We want to build a car,' adds Lisa, 'but it's not going so well.'

'Hmm. I'd rather read my newspaper.'

'Please, Daddy,' plead the children with sweet voices.

'All right, I will,' replies Daddy, 'since you are asking so nicely.'

Giggling, the children pull Daddy by his hands to the play room. The floor is covered with blocks. Daddy looks for a place and sits down. He inspects the blocks. 'OK, look. Where shall we start…?'

In a short while Daddy has put together four wheels and a car body. The children look at him in wonder.

'Here, Daddy, maybe you can use this screwdriver there,' suggests John.

Daddy shakes his head. 'No, this car doesn't have any screws,' and he continues building. Disappointed, John lays the screwdriver down. 'Oh, Daddy,' says Lisa, 'if you make a little bed here in the car, the children could take naps.'

'Take naps? Hey, this is a race car,' laughs Daddy. 'Do you think you take naps in a race car?'

'A race car? But I don't want that at all,' complains Lisa.

'Spoilsport,' teases Daddy, and he builds steadily on. He's all tied up in his car.

The children look unhappily at Daddy. They don't think this is nice at all.

After a while Daddy's car is done.

'Take a look at that!' he says proudly.

But the children have been playing in the garden for some time already.

'Oh well,' says Daddy. And he begins to build a spaceship.

FLEAS

John and Nosey are sitting in the garden. They have played for a long time and now they are resting. They are so dirty!

Nosey begins to scratch himself.

'What's wrong, Nosey?'

Nosey scratches behind his ear. He scratches his side. He scratches his neck.

Mummy comes into the garden.

'Mummy, what's wrong with Nosey?'

Mummy looks into the dog's fur and sees fleas.

'Oh yes, I have to put a flea collar on you, Nosey,' she says.

A little later Nosey has a flea collar on.

'Now the fleas will disappear quickly,' laughs Mummy. She scratches Nosey's head.

Nosey and John sit side by side again.

But wait! What's that itching his back? John begins to scratch his back. And now his hair! He runs fast to Mummy.

'Mummy, Mummy, I think that I need to have a flea collar too! I'm itching all over.'

'Let's take a look,' says Mummy. She looks in John's hair.

'I don't see anything,' she laughs. 'It's just your imagination that makes you itch. That happens sometimes if you think too much about fleas. You know what? You are really dirty. I'll put you in the bath and give you a good scrub. After that I'll give you a collar.'

'So I have to have a flea collar,' asks John, frightened.

'No, dear. I meant a necklace made of sweets,' laughs Mummy.

John doesn't find that so bad at all!

THE GLASS HOUSE

Daddy is whistling while he takes a shower. He's worked hard today and is feeling great. Behind the house, beside the flower bed, he's built a greenhouse. He will grow juicy tomatoes in it. Just the thought of them makes his mouth water.

Outside, a car stops. It's Mummy with the children.

'Lisa, shall we play football?' Daddy hears John say.

Daddy is scared. Football? Oh no!

Soon the children are kicking the ball around the garden. He must warn them!

Dripping wet, he jumps out of the shower. He wraps a towel around himself. Then he runs like crazy out of the bathroom and down the stairs, toward the back door in the kitchen.

Whoops! His wet feet slip on the slippery kitchen floor.

His towel flies up in the air.

Oh, no! He loses his footing and falls down.

Moaning with pain, Daddy stands up and limps to the back door.

While he hops on one leg into the garden, he yells, 'Don't do that!'

The children stand still in fear.

'I've just…built…that greenhouse. You might break the glass with your ball,' he says.

It's totally silent.

Daddy hesitates and looks at himself.

Oh, yes – there he stands, on one leg, dripping wet, with no clothes on.

'Hello, dear,' laughs Mummy.

'Look who I brought.'

Grannie comes from behind the corner. 'Hello, son,' she laughs, playfully. 'Nice greenhouse you have there.'

Daddy's face gets as red as a beetroot.

Then everybody breaks out laughing. What a silly daddy!

IRONING

Daddy hurt his foot yesterday.

Now he rests his ankle on the bench. It's wrapped in a big bandage.

'It hurts,' he complains.

'Just read the paper,' says Mummy, who is ironing. Behind her there's a basket full of clean clothes that all have to be ironed.

'I've read it all. Is it okay if I just read it once?'

Mummy picks a shirt out of the basket.

'Be careful with that shirt. That's the best one I have.'

'Yes, yes,' laughs Mummy, and she sets the iron on the wrinkled shirt.

'Pssst!,' The iron blasts out steam.

Meanwhile Daddy sits like a little child, pouting. 'It hurts.'

'Watch television,' says Mummy.

Daddy sighs really loudly, like a balloon letting all its air out.

'I don't feel like it.'

'Then read a book or a magazine, but stop complaining,' says Mummy, ironing.

'I don't feel like reading. I want to do something,' grumbles Daddy. 'I'm going crazy here.'

'Soon you'll drive me crazy too,' says Mummy, still working on the shirt.

Then Mummy has an idea. 'Sit up straight,' she says. Puzzled, Daddy does as she asks.

Mummy takes the ironing board, puts it on its lowest height, and sets it in front of Daddy. Then she hands him the iron.

'Now you can do something useful. You'll be busy for an hour with this basket of clothes. And I can do something else. Oh, and… be careful with that shirt. It's your best one.'

SAND

After a busy day of work, Mummy comes home.

The children are already home. She hears their voices in the living room.

When she walks into the hall, she sees a little trail of sand.

Sighing, Mummy gets the hoover out of the closet. She plugs it in and turns it on.

'Whoosh,' there goes the white sand up the long hose of the hoover.

'There,' says Mummy while she unplugs it.

But what is that? Another pile of sand.

Mummy plugs it in again, annoyed. The hoover sucks the sand up greedily.

Then Mummy sees one of John's shoes. Around it she sees a little pile of sand.

'Oh, no,' moans Mummy loudly, 'not more sand.'

She drags the hoover further on down the hall and sucks up the white sand. Then she sees the other shoe lying in front of the door of the living room. When she picks it

up, a bunch of sand falls out.

'That's about enough,' grumbles Mummy. She walks into the living room, angry. There's John, playing with stickers.

'Mummy, do you know what we did at school today?' he asks.

'Yes,' says Mummy sternly, 'you played in the sand.'

John look surprised.

'How do you know that?'

'I know a lot more,' continues Mummy, still cross. 'When you came home, you walked through the hall. While you walked, sand dropped out of your shoes. Then you took one of your shoes off and shook the sand out of it. Then you did the same thing with the other.'

John is speechless.

Such a mummy!

She knows everything!

80

MARBLES

Lisa has borrowed a marble from John. It's John's most beautiful marble.

It's blue with little silver stars inside. If you hold it up to the light, it looks like a sapphire. John calls it his super-marble.

Lisa has very nicely asked if she could take it to school today to play with.

That's okay with John, because he thinks Lisa is the nicest sister in the world....

'But,' thinks John later, 'maybe Lisa will lose a game of marbles. Then she'll have to give my marble away. And then I'll lose my super-marble! Oh, I wish I hadn't loaned it to Lisa. How can I have been so dumb? Actually, it's Lisa's fault. Why did she want so badly to borrow the marble? Doesn't she have enough marbles of her own?'

School is out. Lisa comes running over to John. 'Oh no,' thinks John sadly. 'Now she's going to tell me that she's lost my super-marble in a game.'

'Hey, John,' cries Lisa excitedly. 'Here is your super-marble back. Super-thanks, really!'

'Ooof,' thinks John relieved. He sticks his super-marble in his pocket.

Lisa digs in her jacket pocket. She brings out five more marbles.

'Here,' laughs Lisa, excitedly. 'These are for you. I won them with your super-marble!'

'Wow!' says John, surprised. He takes the marbles happily. Are they ever beautiful.

John thinks that's really nice of Lisa.

She really is the nicest sister in the world!

BELLA THE COW

John and Lisa are at Farmer Pete's farm.

Farmer Pete is a friendly man. He often lets the children help with the farm work.

They love that.

They have brought Nosey with them.

'What a nice puppy,' laughs Farmer Pete. He scratches Nosey's head.

'If you like, you can feed the chickens.'

The children get the chicken feed. Nosey runs after them.

They go to the chicken coop and throw the grain on the ground. The chickens come running fast and begin to peck at the food.

Then Nosey sees the chickens. He suddenly begins to bark. The chickens are terrified and try to fly away. Nosey chases them.

'Nosey!' yells Lisa. 'Don't do that!' But Nosey doesn't listen. He keeps chasing the chickens.

Then Lisa sees that the chicken coop door is still open. It's not going to take long before the chickens fly out of the coop, with Nosey right behind.

Then Nosey sees the sheep in the meadow. Barking loudly, he runs toward them. The sheep run away from the noisy little dog. He feels like he's the king of the farm.

Then he sees Sparkle, the cat. Growling and barking, he storms over to her.

Sparkle runs into a stall. Nosey runs into the stall too.

Suddenly there is a huge animal right in front of his nose!

'Mooooo!' says the animal. Nosey jumps with fright. 'Mooooo!' says the cow again.

Yelping, Nosey runs out of the stall.

'Ha-ha-ha,' laughs Farmer Pete. 'He's just met Bella! She doesn't like to fool around.'

Nosey has noticed that. When he comes back to visit the farm again, he'll be a bit better behaved.

POLICE

The children are doing errands with Daddy. They have to go by the police station.

'Will you two wait on this bench?' Daddy asks, while he goes up to the counter.

John and Lisa don't like the police station at all. There are pictures of criminals on the walls.

'What is Daddy doing here?' whispers John to Lisa.

Lisa shrugs her shoulders.

She watches Daddy anxiously. He is talking with the policeman at the counter. She can't hear what they are saying.

Then the policeman looks at the children.

Lisa closes her eyes.

All sorts of ideas run through her head.

'Maybe Daddy brought us here because we ate up that whole bag of biscuits last week,' she whispers worriedly.

'Do we have to go to prison?' asks John fearfully.

'I don't know….'

The policeman keeps looking at the children. It feels like there's cold air on Lisa's back.

Then the policeman comes out from behind the counter. He walks over to the children with Daddy. His handcuffs clink as he walks.

'Oh dear,' stammers Lisa. 'Do we have to go to prison?' Daddy laughs.

'Why should you two go to prison? You are such wonderful children. I just wanted to introduce you to Rick, an old friend of mine.'

The policeman gives each of them a lollipop. His face suddenly seems much friendlier.

While the two men go on talking, the children lick their lollipops.

'Did you hear what Daddy said?' whispers Lisa. 'We are wonderful children. If he only knew….'

BUILDING LAND

It is a beautiful spring day. Lisa and Daddy have been to visit Grannie and Grandad. On the way back, Daddy asks, 'Shall I show you where we used to play all the time when I was a boy?'

Lisa thinks that's a great idea.

They ride until they finally come to a big field. A big, dark orange sign stands on the edge of the field.

'LAND FOR SALE FOR NEW BUILDINGS,' reads Lisa.

Noisy bulldozers, cranes and big lorries are busy getting the land ready. They dig holes in the ground, and pour concrete in. Men in yellow helmets are building walls.

'This is where you played, Daddy?' asks Lisa. Daddy stands looking at the field, speechless.

'Uh… yes,' he answers, slowly. 'There were woods here. Behind them was a pond. In the summer we swam there. When evening came, we listened to the frogs croaking. In the winter, you could skate on the pond…. But now that's all gone forever. Why do they….'

A huge lorry loaded with dirt drives by. Because of its noise, Lisa can't hear Daddy, but she knows why he looks so sad.

'Can you imagine what it was like here before, Lisa?' asks Daddy.

'It must have been beautiful,' she says gently.

'Yes, very beautiful,' sighs Daddy.

A short while later they get back on their bikes. Daddy doesn't say anything.

'Daddy doesn't like land developers,' thinks Lisa.

Tractor

Spring has sprung. You can see it in the trees and plants, where tiny buds are growing. And the grass in the meadow is beginning to get back its colour.

Farmer Pete has taken his tractor out of the barn. Behind the tractor he has attached a plough. It looks like a giant rake with big teeth. Farmer Pete drives over the land with the plough. It loosens all the dead grass to make room for new grass to grow.

John and Lisa come over to help. In the cabin of the tractor there are two little seats. They are perfect for them. They ride over the field with Farmer Pete. They love it.

They sing songs as they go.

Around the tractor birds are fluttering.

'They know that when I plough, they can find food,' explains Farmer Pete. 'They peck at the clumps of grass, looking for worms.'

Farmer Pete knows a lot about animals.

When they finish ploughing, it's time to put plant food on the field.

Farmer Pete attaches a big machine to the tractor. He fills it with plant food that will make the grass grow fast.

When it's full, they drive the tractor to the field.

John and Lisa are fascinated as they watch the plant food get sprinkled on the grass.

'As soon as it rains,' says Farmer Pete, 'the plant food will melt into the ground. It will give the grass what it needs to grow.'

It's so much fun.

The tractor chugs along while John and Lisa enjoy the fine spring sunshine.

A Visitor in the Garden

'Woof! Woof! Grrr!' Barking and growling, Nosey stands by a bush in the back yard.

Curious, John and Lisa run over. 'What is it, Nosey?' asks John.

'John, watch out!' cries Lisa. 'Maybe there's a snake in the bush!' John stands very still.

Lisa quickly grabs a broom out of the garden shed and creeps up to the bush with it.

Nosey keeps on barking like crazy.

Lisa pokes the bush with the broom. Nothing to see. But what's over there on the ground?

A round, rough thing lies there.

Carefully, Lisa touches it with the broomstick. 'Tock-tock.' Nothing happens.

Then Lisa sees what this mysterious thing is.

'Stop barking, Nosey. It's a turtle. You're scaring it with your barking.'

Nosey stops barking immediately.

The children sit beside the terrified turtle. He's pulled his head and feet into his shell.

After a long while, he dares to stick his head out. A pleasant surprise awaits him.

Lisa has gotten him a leaf of lettuce. At school, she learned that turtles love lettuce.

Hesitantly, the turtle pushes his feet out of his shell and creeps toward the lettuce. Nosey and the children watch the turtle eat it up. His slitty eyes blink with pleasure.

'He came here just to visit our back yard,' says John.

'Well, he's very welcome,' laughs Lisa. 'We have plenty of lettuce!'

COLLAR

It's bedtime for John. He goes to the bathroom to take off his clothes.

First he takes of his socks and pants. Then he wants to take off his jumper. He wants to pull it over his head with his short little arms. But it doesn't go so well. The jumper gets stuck, just above his eyebrows.

Then Daddy comes in.

'Daddy, will you help me take off my jumper?' asks John.

'Of course,' says Daddy, and he grabs the jumper. 'What's this? I can't get your jumper off.'

John's head is stuck in the collar.

Daddy tries a second time.

It still doesn't work.

'This is crazy,' grumbles Daddy. 'Has your head grown? I can't get it through the neck of your jumper.'

John looks at Daddy unhappily. The jumper is stuck over his eyebrows. He looks like he's wearing some kind of helmet.

'I'll try one last time,' says Daddy. 'Hold still, okay?'

He pulls so hard on the jumper that John's feet come off the floor. It hurts John. 'Stop, Daddy, stop!' he cries.

Mummy comes into the bathroom.

'What's going on here?' she asks, worried.

'We can't get this jumper off his head,' says Daddy, putting John back on the floor.

'But you don't do it that way,' cries Mummy angrily.

Very softly and carefully, Mummy slides the jumper up, bit by bit

'See, that's how you do it.' John's head slips out of the jumper.

'Whoof!' says John. What if Mummy hadn't come?

BUBBLE DIVING

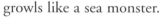

Mummy has made a bubble bath for the children. They love bubble baths.

'Look,' says John. He puts some bubbles on his chin. 'I'm an old man with a long beard.'

Lisa puts a pile of bubbles on her hair.

'What do you think of my new hat, sir?' They are having a ball.

The children swirl around in the warm water, making more bubbles.

They push all the bubbles to one side. Now they want to go bubble diving! That's a new sport – just discovered!

First it's Lisa's turn. She closes her eyes and pushes her face deep into the bubbles. When she comes up, she looks like a bubble monster. White clouds of bubbles cover her head as she growls like a sea monster.

They beat up more bubbles and push them to one side again. Now it's John's turn. He pinches his nose shut and closes his eyes. With a spring, he dives into the bubbles. Water and bubbles fly all over. Half the bathroom is flooded.

'John! What are you doing?' cries Lisa, shocked.

John wipes the bubbles out of his eyes. He sees the huge puddle on the bathroom floor.

Just at that moment, Mummy comes into the bathroom.

'What does this mean?' she exclaims crossly.

'We've found a new sport – bubble diving – and then….'

'Bubble diving?' snorts Mummy. 'Well, now you have another new sport to try – floor drying. It's not as much fun, but….'

LETTER

'The post man is here!' calls Daddy.

'Who wants to go to the post box?'

John and Lisa's house on top of the hill, but Daddy has put the post box at the bottom to make it easier for the post man. Every day the children have to make a run for the post box, but they like to do that.

Today it's Lisa's turn to run to the post box.

'A letter from Aunt Bonnie and Uncle Bob!' yells Lisa, before she's even back in the house. She gives the letter to Mummy, who quickly opens it.

'What's inside?' the children want to know.

'Tomorrow Aunt Bonnie and Uncle Bob are taking the train to our village. They will stay with us a few days. Aunt Bonnie's doctor says she needs to take a rest. And where can she do that better than with us?'

That's great! Aunt Bonnie and Uncle Bob are really nice.

'Could they stay in your room for a few days, Lisa?' asks Mummy.

Oooh! Suddenly Lisa feels Aunt Bonnie and Uncle Bob are a little less nice.

'In my room?' she protests.

'Well, yes, since we don't have a guest room. That's the only solution.'

'Where do I have to sleep then?'

'You can sleep on an air mattress in John's room,' says Mummy.

A smile glides over Lisa's face. Sleeping in her brother's bedroom… that will be a riot!

She helps Mummy get out the air mattress. She asks Mummy to get out the sleeping bag and flashlight, too.

It will be just like going camping! Fun!

Lisa can hardly wait until the guests get there….

HOUSE GUESTS

Lisa and John are all excited because today Aunt Bonnie and Uncle Bob will come to visit for a few days. The children think that is fantastic, because they love Aunt Bonnie and Uncle Bob.

Daddy drives to the station to fetch them.

Meanwhile Lisa and John help Mummy in the kitchen.

She makes a big plate of chicken. It smells great. Lisa washes the vegetables and cuts them in small slices. Now and then she nibbles a little piece of tomato or cucumber.

That's okay with Mummy. There is more than enough.

John carefully stirs the sauce, so it doesn't burn. But he can't taste it, because it's too hot.

When everything is ready, they set the table.

Mummy gets her beautiful tablecloth with sunflowers on it out of the linen drawer.

She and Lisa lay it out on the table and smooth out the small wrinkles.

While Lisa folds the napkins, John and Mummy begin to set the table.

After it's set with plates and glasses and silverware, they put a big bunch of flowers on the table.

So! Everything is ready. Just in time, because here comes Daddy's car.

The children run outside.

Lots of kissing and hugging goes on. Then they all go inside.

'Oh, isn't that beautiful,' exclaims Aunt Bonnie when she sees the table.

The children beam with pride as Mummy tells Aunt Bonnie how much they helped her get it ready.

Then John and Lisa see two huge presents that Uncle Bob has with him.

It's certainly going to be a great day!

91

SPACE HOPPERS

Do you know what Uncle Bob's presents were? In each package there is a space hopper. A red one for John and a yellow one for Lisa.

Sitting on the huge balls and yelling, the children are bouncing and bumping around in the garden.

Uncle Bob laughs as he watches.

'Don't get Uncle Bob dirty,' Aunt Bonnie warns the children.

'Shall we have a race?' asks Uncle Bob. 'Who can get to the bottom of the hill first?'

The children love the idea.

'Go!' yells Uncle Bob. They bounce down the hill. Boy, can they go fast!

But - oh, no! Lisa bumps into John.

'Watch out!' he yells. Too late. The children fall

off their balls and roll downhill. The huge balls bounce along ahead of them.

At the bottom of the hill John and Lisa finally stop. Just in time. Otherwise they could have fallen into the brook.

'Did I hurt you?' Lisa asks her little brother.

'No,' laughs John. 'I thought it was fun!'

Uncle Bob comes running after them, worried. But he starts slipping down the hill as he runs. With a loud splash, he falls into the icy water of the brook!

Happily the brook isn't very deep, and Uncle Bob climbs out quickly.

'Are you two okay?' he asks, through chattering teeth. His clothes are muddy and dripping wet.

'We're fine,' laughs Lisa. 'But you're going to get a good scolding from Aunt Bonnie!'

MAGIC WITH UNCLE BOB

Uncle Bob can do magic tricks really well. He puts a handkerchief over his hand, blows on it, and pulls a whole bouquet of flowers out. John thinks magic tricks are wonderful. Sometimes Uncle Bob pulls a coin from behind John's ear. John gets to keep it. Other times Uncle Bob does some quick magician movements and pulls a sweet out of John's hair. John gets to keep that too. He feels his hair, hoping to find more sweets, but never finds any.

'I can do tricks too,' says John one day to Uncle John.

'I'd really like to see that.'

'Look: what do I have in my hand?'

'Nothing,' answers Uncle Bob.

'Close your eyes and count to ten and I'll say a magic word.'

Uncle Bob closes his eyes and counts to ten out loud.

'Sim-salabim-salabom!' says John. Quickly he pulls his t-shirt up and pulls a piece of paper out.

'Ten!' finishes Uncle Bob, and opens his eyes.

John shows Uncle Bob the piece of paper.

'What's that?' wonders Uncle Bob.

'A picture I've drawn for you,' laughs John.

It's a lovely picture of Uncle Bob, holding a tall magician's hat and a magic wand. He's pulling a white bunny out of the hat.

'Oh, thank you, my little friend,' laughs Uncle Bob, and he gives John a big hug.

'Hey! What's going on here?' Suddenly he pulls a sweet out of John's hair. 'That was in your hair. It's for you,' he laughs.

Quickly, John feels his hair. What a pity. No more sweets in there....

SAYING GOODBYE

Today Aunt Bonnie and Uncle Bob go home. Daddy has loaded their suitcases into the car.

John and Lisa stand by, watching.

After they say goodbye to Mummy, Aunt Bonnie and Uncle Bob come to the children. 'You look very sad,' says Uncle Bob.

'We don't want you to go home,' wails Lisa.

'That's really sweet of you,' laughs Aunt Bonnie. 'But we can't stay away from home forever. We have to get a nursery ready soon.' She points to her tummy.

'A nursery? But you don't have any children,' says Lisa, surprised. Then she smiles.

'You're going to have a baby!' she cries happily.

Now John gets it. Wonderful! They are going to have a new cousin!

'But how did the baby get in Aunt Bonnie's tummy?' he asks himself. 'It must be another magic trick.'

'Can you see it already?' asks Lisa.

'A little,' laughs Aunt Bonnie, and she holds her shirt tight against her tummy. And sure enough, Lisa can see it. Her tummy is a bit round.

'Will it be a boy or a girl?' she wants to know.

'That's our little secret,' says Uncle Bob firmly. 'You'll have to wait and see.'

'We've got to go now,' says Daddy, 'or else you'll miss your train.'

Aunt Bonnie and Uncle Bob give the children big kisses and get into the car. John and Lisa wave until the car disappears from sight.

'Bye, Uncle Bob. Bye, Aunt Bonnie. Bye, sweet little baby!'

PIGLETS

The telephone rings. It is Farmer Pete. 'Hefty has had piglets. If you would like to see them, you are welcome.'

He doesn't have to say that twice.

A bit later the whole family stands by Hefty's stall.

'The piglets are already a few days old,' explains Farmer Pete. 'I waited to tell you about them because they need lots of rest in their first days.'

Hefty hears Farmer Pete's voice. She gets up and comes over to see the visitors. Behind her wobble tiny pink piglets. There are six of them.

Lisa is crazy about them and wants to see them better. She climbs on the little fence.

'Careful, sweetie,' says Mummy. 'You could fall.'

Lisa acts as if she hasn't heard Mummy and leans as far over the fence as she can to see the little piglets. They follow their mother through the mud and straw. They make such cute sounds!

Lisa wants to pet a piglet. She leans as far as she can over the fence to grab one.

'Lisa, don't do that,' says Mummy again. 'You're going to fall in a second.'

But Lisa stubbornly goes on leaning over. She has almost touched a piglet. Her fingers almost reach his nose.

Then in a second she tumbles head over heels right into the mud. The piglets all squeal and they run away. Lisa begins to squeal too.

She is shocked by the noise the piglets make and her skirt is full of mud.

That's what comes of not listening. It's her own fault! Talk about being pig-headed....

97

LEAK

to know where that drip is coming from.

Then he sees it. Up above, there's a metal pipe. A little drop of water hangs from it, and in a few seconds, it swells into a big, fat drop. With a loud 'Tick' it drops right by the door to the elf's house and splashes in front of his feet.

'What a nuisance,' he grumbles. 'I'm not going to get a wink of sleep tonight.'

Above, Mummy and Daddy are sound asleep.

The door opens and tiny elf feet tiptoe into the room….

It's the middle of the night. Tiny Elf is awakened by an annoying noise.

'Tick!'

Now it's quiet. 'Tick!'

Tiny Elf has had enough and goes to look. He opens the door. A loud 'Tick' sounds and a drop of water falls right into his collar!

Oh boy, is that cold! And wet!

Tiny Elf hurries inside to get a torch. He wants

When Daddy sits down for breakfast, he says, 'I dreamt last night that an elf came and told me I have a leak in my water pipes. He said I need to call a plumber. It's a bad leak.'

John and Lisa look at each other.

'I just went to take a look, and do you know what? There really was a leak. I've called the plumber.'

'What a strange dream,' says Mummy.

John and Lisa aren't so sure it really was a dream….

NOSEY THE SUPERNOSE

Nosey is having an adventure in the garden.

He imagines that he is a big, strong dog named Supernose instead of a little black one named Nosey.

Supernose sniffs in the garden, looking for signs of intruders. What has his sharp nose smelled? A fresh scent!

Supernose goes on investigating.

The scent leads right to the garden shed. He stops at the door and pushes his nose against it. The door swings open. Supernose bares his teeth and creeps like a real hunting dog inside the shed. The door swings slowly shut behind him.

Although very little light comes through the windows, Supernose sees his prey: a tiny grey mouse.

The mouse has seen Supernose. He races past and dashes out the door just as it closes.

Boom. The door shuts tight.

Nosey tries to open the door with his paw, but that doesn't work. The door is locked. Nosey sits in prison....

The dog scratches as hard as he can on the door, but it stays shut.

He begins to bark. Nobody hears Nosey.

A little later it gets dark. Long shadows fall through the windows of the garden shed. Nosey is really scared now. He imagines that a huge hoard of grey mice will sneak into the garden shed to teach him a lesson. He begins to howl with fear.

Then the door swings open. 'Here you are! I've looked all over for you!' he hears Lisa saying, full of worry. With a huge spring, Nosey jumps into Lisa's arms.

Supernose Nosey is back to being an ordinary, small black dog....

BUMMEL

John is playing in his room with Bummel, his teddy bear. He's playing hide and seek. First he hides his bear. Then he acts as if he's forgotten where his bear is, and goes looking for him.

This time he's hidden his bear well. He's just going to start looking for him when he hears footsteps coming up the stairs.

It's Lisa. 'Would you like to go shopping with Mummy and me?' she asks. 'After that we can go visit Grannie and Grandad.'

Naturally, John wants to go along. They run downstairs together.

It's very late when they get home.

'Hop in the bath, and then put your pyjamas on and jump into bed,' says Mummy, turning on the water.

When John crawls into bed, he can't find Bummel.

This time he's really forgotten where he hid him. John looks all over, but doesn't see his bear anywhere.

'John, it's late,' says Mummy. 'You've really got to get to bed. Tomorrow you must go to school. You can sleep just one night without your teddy bear. I'm sure that we'll find him tomorrow.'

With a shrug, John crawls under the covers. The bed is empty without Bummel.

After a while Mummy and Daddy get ready for bed. When Mummy pulls back the covers, there lies Bummel, in the middle of their bed. 'You were really hidden well this time,' she tells the teddy bear. 'I know somebody who is really missing you.'

Mummy tiptoes into John's bedroom and lays Bummel softly next to the boy in the bed. John throws an arm around the bear and goes on sleeping. Will he ever be happy when he wakes up!

DEAR DIARY

Dear Diary,

I have to tell you something. I'm in love with a boy in my class. His name is Jonas and he's a sweetheart.

Today we were on the playground, playing tag. Jonas was 'it' and he chased after me. Just when he almost caught me, I tripped and fell smack on the ground. It hurt a lot and my right knee was bleeding.

Jonas helped me sit up.

When he saw my knee was bloody, he grabbed his handkerchief from his pocket and put it on my cut.

'You need to get a plaster on that,' he said gently. 'I'll bring you to the office.'

Jonas held me up and then I hopped to the office on one leg. When we got there, I had to go to the nurse's office and get cleaned up.

Jonas stayed with me the whole time. He held my hand while she cleaned my cut. It stung a lot.

Because it hurt I squeezed Jonas' hand really hard, but he didn't mind. He is really strong.

When my cut was all cleaned out and bandaged, I had to stay sitting in the nurse's office for a while. Jonas stayed by me and told me jokes. We laughed so much!

Then he gave me a lollipop. 'Here – you can have it,' he told me. I didn't eat the lollipop. I'm going to save it to remember Jonas. If only all boys were like Jonas.

APRIL FOOLS!

Today is April Fools' Day.

John and Lisa have drawn two fish on some coloured paper. They have cut them out and attached the fish to strings with a bit of sticky tape.

They want to fool Mummy and Daddy.

Daddy and Mummy are sitting at the table, reading the newspapers.

As quietly as a mouse, Lisa slips behind her parents. She sticks the first fish on the back of Daddy's shirt. Daddy goes on reading the paper, not noticing anything.

Then Lisa sticks a fish on Mummy's back. She also doesn't notice a thing.

The children run away as fast as they can.

After a while Mummy and Daddy stand up.

'Hey,' says Daddy, 'what's that on your back?'

Mummy feels her back with her hand. Her fingers find the string. She pulls the sticky tape loose. She sees the fish dangling from the string.

'April Fool!' is written on the fish.

'Ha, ha, ha,' laughs Daddy. 'You've been fooled! It's the first of April!'

'Don't laugh too soon,' says Mummy after she recovers from her surprise. 'It looks like you've caught a fish too.'

Daddy's laughing spell is quickly over. He feels his back.

Yes indeed. Daddy also discovers a fish on his back.

Lisa and John have watched all of this from a distance. They laugh and laugh.

That was fun!

TINY ELF'S TROUSERS

'Pssst! Lisa!'

Sleepily, Lisa opens her eyes. Who is waking her up so early?

'It's me, Tiny Elf,' whispers a small voice. 'You've got to help me.' Lisa sits up in bed.

'Why don't you have any trousers on?' she asks, still drowsy.

'That's the problem. I can't find my trousers anywhere,' grumbles the elf. 'You have to help me look. Last night I hung them on the clothesline. When I went to get them this morning, they were gone. My trousers have been stolen!'

'Stolen?' asks Lisa, surprised. 'Or else… wait a minute….' Lisa slips out of bed.

'I think I might know who the thief is.'

She picks up the elf and takes him to Nosey, who is sleeping downstairs in his basket. And sure enough, there are the trousers. Nosey has torn them to shreds.

'Oh, no,' wails the elf, 'my beautiful trousers. Now I don't have any. What can I do now?'

Still sleepy, Lisa runs a hand through her hair. Then she has a terrific idea.

Quickly she goes to her room and looks through all her toys.

'Look what I've found for you,' laughs Lisa, when she comes back downstairs later.

She shows the elf a pair of red and white striped trousers for her doll. 'I think they are exactly

your size.'

Quick as a flash, the elf puts the trousers on. They fit perfectly.

'Now I don't need new trousers at all. These are wonderful!' he cries happily.

'Thanks so much, Lisa. You are a real friend,' he beams, and gives her a big kiss.

DEAR DIARY

Dear Diary,

Mummy has asked Daddy if he can hang up a hook in the bathroom.
'Of course, I'm a true handyman,' he says. Mummy begins to laugh.
With a pencil Daddy draws a cross on the wall, exactly where Mummy
wants the hook to hang.
With his electric drill, he starts drilling a hole in the wall.
Wham! The drill stops suddenly. Daddy wants to pull it out of the hole,
but he can't. He's got to free it. With two hands, he pulls as hard as he can.
The drill suddenly slides out of the hole and Daddy falls backward, exactly
on top of Mummy. They fall into the bath together. Luckily they aren't hurt
at all.

But what is that? Water is squirting out of the hole. First a little bit, then a
big stream, right on top of Mummy and Daddy, in the bath.
'Oh, no,' cries Mummy, 'you've drilled a hole in the water pipe!'
Daddy and Mummy try to climb out of the bath, but the water is spraying
right in their faces.
'Put your finger over the hole,' gasps Daddy. 'I'll go turn off the water.'
While Daddy runs to do that, Mummy tries to stop up the hole in the pipe,
but the water sprays all over.
Finally the spray stops. Mummy is soaking wet. Her hair hangs in long
snakes all over her face. She doesn't look very happy.
This is certainly the last time she is going to ask Daddy to be a handyman!

New Jacket

Lisa is wearing a new jacket to school today.
'Be careful not to get it dirty,' calls Mummy as Lisa leaves for school.

At the school playground, a classmate cries, 'Hey, Lisa, will you play ball-tag with me?'
'Of course,' answers Lisa, 'but let me take off my new jacket so it won't get dirty.'
A moment later, the children are playing a new game, called ball-tag. Tom is 'it.' He chases his friends, holding a big, bouncy ball. If he can throw the ball and hit one of them with it, they are 'it' next. But they can punch it away with their fists and not be 'it.' Tom throws the ball, but he misses again and again.

Then he chases Lisa. She runs as fast as she can. But then she does something dumb. She runs into a corner of the playground. Too late, she realizes that she can't get away. She backs up to the wall and balls up her fists.

Tom holds the ball over his head and throws with all his might.

Boom! With a tremendous blow of her fists, Lisa bangs the ball high in the air above her. With a loud noise, it slams into the edge of the roof above her. An old piece of the roof breaks off, and down it comes, with a stream of dirty water and old leaves.

Before she realizes what's happening, Lisa is drenched in dirty, cold water.

She can't go to school like that.
Luckily the school has extra clothes in case of accidents like this one.

Poor Lisa. That was a cold shower! But happily, her new jacket is still clean....

BIGGIE AND THE BIRD

One day a little bird lands in the chicken pen. He pecks at grains here and there on the ground.

'Hey,' says Biggie the rooster, surprised to see the bird. 'What sort of bird are you?'

'I'm a sparrow,' says the clever bird.

'Would you like to come and live with us?' asks Biggie, curiously.

'No, thanks!' laughs the sparrow. 'I just want to come and eat. Is that okay?'

'Of course,' says Biggie. The tiny bird pecks at grain after grain. Biggie runs after him.

'Where do you live?' Biggie wants to know.

'I have a nest in the pear tree,' answers the sparrow.

'In a tree?' asks Biggie, shocked. 'Don't you have a coop?'

'Me? A coop?' laughs the sparrow. 'No way, silly. I'm a free bird.'

'Wow,' answers Biggie. 'You are... free?'

'Yes,' continues the sparrow, 'I fly and land wherever I want.'

'But... how do you get your food?'

'Oh, I get it here and there,' laughs the sparrow. 'I always find something to eat.'

'Even in winter, when everything is under the snow?'

'Hmm. In the winter it's harder. Now and then in the winter we get really hungry.'

Biggie has to think this over. 'Sometimes you don't get enough to eat,' he thinks. 'That's awful.'

'You have to always look out for cats and other animals that might want to eat you,' adds the sparrow.

Cats? Animals that want to eat YOU?

Biggie is suddenly very happy that he lives in the chicken coop. It's safe and twice every day he gets fed. Without doing anything!

What a life!

BIRD HOUSE

Daddy and John are in the garden shed. They are building a bird house.

Spring has arrived. In a few more days all the birds will be looking for places to nest and start their new families. John and Daddy hope that one bird family will come and live in the house they are making.

While Daddy nails the last piece in place, John looks among the paint cans to find a good colour to paint the house.

'Have you found a good one yet?' asks Daddy. 'The house is ready to paint.'

'I want red,' says John. 'My favourite colour.'

'Then we'll pick red, okay?'

'Do you think the birds like red too, Daddy?'

'Of course. There are so many kinds of birds. There's got to be one kind that likes red.'

After the birdhouse is painted a beautiful red and hung in the pear tree, John and Daddy stand admiring it.

It doesn't take long before the first pair of birds comes flying by. Curious, they investigate the house. Then they fly away.

'Maybe they don't think our birdhouse is nice,' says John.

'Let's just wait for the next flock,' says Daddy.

The same two birds come flying by again. This time though, both birds have twigs in their beaks.

'Hey,' says Daddy, surprised. 'They have picked our birdhouse. Look, they're beginning to build their nest.'

John and Daddy stay proudly watching the birds for a long time as they bring straw and twigs to build their nest.

Everyone likes the new birdhouse!

WALDORF

When Lisa comes outside one morning, she finds a surprise. A big red cat is sitting in front of the house.

'Meow,' says the cat as he walks over to Lisa.

'Hello, kitty,' says Lisa. 'What are you doing here?'

'Meow, meow,' answers the cat, rubbing against Lisa's legs.

'Are you hungry?'

The cat meows louder. 'I'll go get you something to eat as fast as I can.'

The cat keeps on meowing impatiently while he waits for Lisa to come back.

There she is again. John and Mummy are with her too.

Mummy sets a plate with scraps down for the cat. The cat gobbles up the scraps while the children watch him.

'What a sweet cat,' says Lisa. 'Is he a runaway?'

'Who knows,' says Mummy. 'Maybe he's abandoned. We'll take good care of him. Maybe his owner will come here looking for him. Then we can give him back.'

The children like that idea.

Here comes Nosey. He wants to see what's going on.

Suddenly the cat growls and his fur stands on end. He hisses between his teeth: 'Pssst!'

Nosey is scared. Oooh, he'd rather not be around that cat!

'What should we call the cat?' asks Lisa. 'Is it a boy or a girl?'

'He's a boy,' says Mummy. 'He's a tom cat.'

'Then we'll call him Waldorf,' John proposes.

'Why Waldorf?' asks Lisa.

'Just because. I think it sounds nice.'

'Okay, that's it,' laughs Mummy. 'Welcome to our house on the hill, Waldorf.'

THE MONSTER

Tiny Elf can't sleep. He tosses and turns a hundred times, left and right. Then he gives up and gets out of bed. He pulls on his dressing gown and gets a glass of milk from the fridge.

He takes a big gulp of milk and sits down at the kitchen table with a sigh.

But what was that? He thinks he hears something outside….

Tiny Elf quickly grabs a broom and slips over to the door. Very carefully, he opens the door a crack. He peers into the darkness, but there is nothing to see….

'I could swear that I heard something,' he mumbles into his beard. He opens the door all the way and takes a cautious step outside. It's pitch dark.

Suddenly two green eyes light up in the dark.

'A monster!!!' yells Tiny Elf, and in shock he darts back inside.

He wants to shut his door tight, but he can't because a hairy paw pushes it roughly open again.

Tiny Elf hides himself in a corner. With sharp claws, the paw sweeps through the living room.

'But…that is a cat's paw,' thinks Tiny Elf fearfully. 'He has invaded my house. I must scare him away.'

Then he gets a terrific idea.

Out of his storage chest he quietly pulls out the water hose and attaches it to a tap. He turns the tap on and points the water stream at the cat's enormous paw.

'Riaow!!!' snarls the cat, and the paw disappears.

'We don't like cats, you hear?' he yells.

It looks like Waldorf has learned a lesson.

ACCIDENT

'Lisa,' asks Mummy, 'would you please go collect the eggs? I haven't had time, and I want to mop the kitchen floor.'

Lisa is glad to do that. She grabs a basket and speeds to the chicken coop.

'Good morning,' says Lisa, as she enters the coop.

'Bok-bok-bagaaaa,' answer the chickens.

'You have done a fine job, you know?' says Lisa, when she sees how many eggs they have laid. There's at least a dozen. She puts them carefully into the basket.

'Thank you very much, ladies,' she says to the hens, who look at her closely. 'Bye for now. See you tomorrow.'

Lisa walks toward the house.

Suddenly John jumps out from behind a bush.

'Your money or your life! I'm a bandit!' he yells.

'John!' cries Lisa. 'You scared me! I almost dropped the egg basket. Mummy would be mad then.'

John shrugs his shoulders and runs away, whooping loudly.

'Wow, that scared me,' thinks Lisa. 'Luckily the eggs are okay.' Very carefully, she opens the kitchen door.

'Mummy,' she calls while she comes in. 'Here are the…aiy-yiii!'

'Watch out! The floor is slippery!' cries Mummy, too late.

Lisa slips on the wet floor.

The egg basket falls and so does Lisa. In a second, she is sitting in a puddle of eggs.

'You poor thing,' comforts Mummy, while she washes a crying Lisa under the shower. 'Don't worry. It was an accident, and accidents happen now and then.'

That's the way it is. If you have an accident, you're just unlucky. Afterward, things usually go better.

AN EGG-TREE

Today the children will have a party at school. So the children are going to make an egg-tree. The teacher brought in branches from a curly willow tree. She stuck them into a pot of sand so it looks like a real tree.

She also brought some eggs. She makes tiny holes in the eggs with a large needle, one hole at the top and one hole at the bottom.

All the children blow hard on their eggs so that the stuff inside comes out without breaking the shells.

They put all the yolks and egg whites in a big bowl.

'Oh, that looks so awful,' laughs John when he sees the bowl.

When all the eggs are empty, the children can decorate the shells.

John colours his egg yellow. It's not easy, and before he's done his fingers are all yellow too. He'll have to wash them later.

With a fine brush John adds some red dots to his egg. Then he lets it dry.

All the children do their very best to decorate their eggs beautifully. It's going to be a wonderful egg-tree.

When all the eggs are dry, the teacher attaches strings to each one. Then the children get to hang their eggs on the branches.

'What a lovely egg-tree!' exclaims the teacher. 'You have done a great job, children. So to reward you, I'll make you a delicious omelette.'

The teacher mixes the egg whites and yolks with some milk and cooks them in a big pan. Soon the room smells wonderful. The children can't wait to eat their omelette.

They made a pretty tree and get to have a nice meal – nothing's wasted!

A BUSY BUNNY

Tiny Elf has a very special guest today. The Easter Bunny is coming by.

Every year the bunny comes to visit his good friend, Tiny Elf. He knows the elf will have a delicious carrot cake waiting for him. It's a nice change from all those chocolate eggs.

'My goodness, I've been busy this year,' he tells Tiny Elf. 'I've already decorated thousands of eggs for the children, and I'm still not done.'

'Will you be able to get them all decorated?' asks Tiny Elf, concerned.

'I could sure use some help,' answers the bunny, taking another bite out of the carrot cake. He thinks Tiny Elf makes the most delicious carrot cake in the world.

Tiny Elf scratches his white beard. 'Maybe I can help you.'

The bunny stops chewing and looks sharply at the elf.

'Why not?' he says. 'Anyone who can make such a good carrot cake can certainly do a good job decorating eggs.'

For the next few hours, all sorts of work goes on in Tiny Elf's house. Before long, a mountain of decorated eggs stands ready to be delivered in front of the door.

The bunny starts loading them into his basket so he can deliver them. He feels so happy now. Before he leaves, he gives Tiny Elf a big wink. He's so glad to have Tiny Elf as an assistant!

BIGGIE ESCAPES

Daddy has forgotten to close the gate to the chicken pen.

Cautiously, Biggie the rooster sticks his head out through the crack to look around. 'I'm going to explore the wide world,' thinks Biggie to himself.

First he carefully tiptoes into the garden.

Then he puffs up and crows, 'Long live freedom!' and dashes from bush to bush. Suddenly, though, he freezes. Right in front of him is Waldorf, the fat tom cat.

'So, my little chicken friend,' purrs the cat, 'are you out for a walk?'

'I… I… I'm a rooster, actually,' stammers Biggie, terrified.

Waldorf bares his sharp teeth and claws. 'That really doesn't matter to me.'

'Uh… well, it does to me,' cries Biggie, and he races away.

Waldorf chases him with huge leaps. Biggie runs as fast as he can toward the street. But just as he gets there, a big lorry zooms by, honking its horn to warn him to get out of the way.

Biggie barely escapes getting hit. He collapses in a heap in a puddle beside the street, scared out of his wits.

Luckily Waldorf is also scared by the lorry, and he stops in his tracks.

Biggie slowly gets up from the puddle. He's soaking wet and his heart is pounding.

He's so scared! He wants to get back to the peace and safety of his chicken coop.

'I'm not staying here a moment longer,' decides Biggie. He runs full speed home to his pen.

Luckily the gate is still open.

Exhausted, Biggie struggles into a warm, cosy nest. One thing's for sure: Biggie will never run away again.

GARDENING

John and Lisa help Daddy. Every day they water the soil so that the seeds have enough to drink.

Now the seedlings are finally popping up. In the trenches that Daddy made, they see tiny green leaves in long rows, side by side. Here and there are little clusters of plants.

'We have to thin out the clumps,' says Daddy. 'From each clump you need to pick just one plant to stay and grow. Take the others out carefully. You can plant them again in another spot where no seeds came up.'

All three of them get busy. They are very careful and take care not to step on the tiny plants.

Here comes Nosey.

He watches while the children and Daddy dig in the ground.

'I can do that, too!' thinks Nosey. He sniffs the soil and begins to dig with his front paws. The earth flies all over.

'Hey, Nosey!' yells Daddy, angrily. 'What are you doing, you naughty dog?'

Nosey looks at Daddy with surprise.

'You are wrecking the little plants, silly. Go on, get out of the garden!'

With his tail between his legs, Nosey leaves.

Poor Nosey. He only wants to help….

Last month Daddy planted all kinds of seeds in the garden.

He made long trenches in the ground. He put the seeds in them and then put the dirt back over them.

Beside each trench he set a little sign so he can tell what kind of vegetable he planted there.

'Lettuce, radishes, carrots….' Lisa can read all the signs.

CHOCOLATE

John and Lisa are sitting with a box of chocolates between them. They have decided to share them.

'Here's one for you,' says Lisa. 'And one for me.'

'Mmm…,' says John. 'It's delicious.'

'And so is this one,' says Lisa. 'At least we know these two are delicious.'

Lisa divides more of the chocolates up and they go on eating. Then they think it's time for a little break.

They have lots of chocolate smears on their mouths and hands.

Lisa picks out some more and shares them with John.

'Let's see if these taste as good as the others,' she says.

The chocolates disappear into the children's mouths.

After a while they have eaten a dozen chocolates each!

John looks a little pale.

'What's the matter, John?' asks Lisa, a bit worried.

'I have a tummy ache,' he moans.

If Lisa is honest, she has to admit she has a strange feeling in her tummy too.

And it's only getting worse! Lisa and John run to Mummy.

'You poor things! So both of you have tummy aches?' asks Mummy with concern. But then she sees the chocolate smears on their mouths and hands. She looks angry and puts her hands on her hips.

'You two have eaten too much chocolate, right?' she asks sternly. 'Then it's your own fault if your tummies ache. Let this be a lesson to you: too much chocolate makes you sick!'

Oh dear, oh dear. Why is chocolate so yummy then?

PLAYMATES

Lisa is visiting her friend.

John sits alone in the garden, feeling cranky.

He wishes his sister was here to play with him instead.

'Hey! Pssst!' he suddenly hears.

John looks around him in surprise.

It's Tiny Elf.

'What's going on?' he asks John.

John sighs. 'I'm feeling cranky. There's nobody to play with.'

Tiny Elf thinks this over, tugging on his white beard.

'What would you think if we played a little football? It's been years since I've played.'

'Oh, yes!' cries John.

'I'll be the goalie,' says the elf.

John gets the ball while the elf puts two sticks into the ground.

'This is the goal, okay?'

'Okay,' yells John, setting the ball on the ground. He gets ready to kick the ball into the goal.

With a tremendous shot, John kicks the ball.

Tiny Elf springs to catch the ball. Boom! The ball knocks him flat on his back.

'Ow! Ow!' he wails.

John flies to his tiny playmate's side. He helps him up and wipes his nose.

'Ow, that hurt. Why did you have to kick it so hard?'

'I'm sorry,' John stammers. 'I suppose you'll never play with me again,' he says mournfully.

Tiny Elf looks angrily at John. His nose is all swollen.

'Right. I'm never going to play football with you again,' says the elf firmly.

'But I will surely play with you in the sand pit!' laughs Tiny Elf.

And so it was a nice afternoon after all....

BABY PHOTO

A letter has come from Aunt Bonnie and Uncle Bob. They are expecting a baby.

With the letter is a picture of the baby. 'How can that be?' Lisa asks Mummy in surprise. 'Is the baby already born?'

'No,' laughs Mummy. 'It's a picture made by an ultrasound.'

Lisa makes a funny face. 'A what?'

'An ultrasound. That is a photo of the baby while it still is in Aunt Bonnie's tummy.'

'How can they do that?' asks John.

'The doctor has a really cool machine. He can use it to see inside Aunt Bonnie's tummy. It doesn't hurt the baby at all,' explains Mummy.

They look at the photo together.

John and Lisa can only see grey and white spots. They don't see a baby anywhere.

Only after Mummy shows them where the head and the feet are can they begin to see something that looks a bit like a baby.

'It looks like an ugly baby,' says John, disappointed.

'That's because it is still such a tiny baby,' laughs Mummy. 'When it's bigger, it will certainly look beautiful.'

'If it's such an ugly baby, why do they take a picture of it?' asks Lisa.

'That way the doctor can see if the baby is healthy. And sometimes you can see if it's a boy or a girl.'

'Oh, what's it going to be, Mummy?' asks Lisa.

'I don't know,' says Mummy. 'Aunt Bonnie writes in her letter that they want to keep that a secret until the baby is born. They think that's much more exciting.'

John and Lisa think so too. They can hardly wait until their cousin is born.

Will it be a boy? Or a girl?

Who knows?

Sea Captain

John has got a toy boat from Daddy. It's a fine boat, and it can float on the water. It has a captain, and he looks like a real seaman.

John takes the boat to the little brook at the bottom of the hill. The brook is just deep enough for John's boat.

'Brrr,' thinks John. 'That water is really cold.'

Carefully he puts his boat in the water and gives it a little push. The brave captain stands on the boat and looks out for danger.

The boat floats downstream. There are big stones in the water and the brook gets narrower, so the water flows faster.

'That's exciting,' thinks John, while the boat gets carried through the rapids. Then the boat hits a rock. The captain wobbles and falls down. Luckily the railing keeps him from falling into the water.

'Oooh, I've got to get my boat out of that water,' thinks John. 'Otherwise the captain could fall overboard. I can't let that happen. Without a captain, a boat can't go anywhere.'

John tries to grab the boat, but it's not easy. The stream is flowing faster than he expected.

Luckily the boat gets stuck on a tiny branch. John sticks out his hand to catch it.

Oh, no! He loses his balance and falls into the cold water with a splash.

Sputtering, he stands up. Luckily the brook isn't deep. And he has saved his boat!

Shivering from cold, John runs back to the house.

Thank goodness the captain didn't fall into the brook too!

A GREEDY BEAST

It's night time.

Waldorf, the red tomcat, walks outside in the moonlight. He jumps up on the kitchen windowsill. Hey – the window is open a bit.

Waldorf uses his head to open the window a little further. Just enough to let himself in.

The cat sniffs the air. Mmm, it smells good in the kitchen. Tomorrow the whole family is going on an outing. Mummy has made all kinds of good things to eat that they will take along with them. Waldorf wants to taste a few….

The next morning Lisa and John hear Mummy talking excitedly.

The children hurry to the kitchen.

'What's going on?' asks Lisa, worried.

Mummy is shaking with anger. She points to the snacks and cakes. There's practically nothing left.

'This is a disaster,' she moans. 'My lovely snacks….' Sadly, she sinks into a chair.

John and Lisa look at the mess.

'Somebody ate all the best things,' says Lisa.

'Yeah, I really wanted one of those cream cakes,' says John hungrily.

Lisa discovers a paw print in the middle of the mess.

'Hey, I recognise this paw print,' she says cleverly.

Lisa runs outside. Curious, John and Mummy follow her.

After a bit of searching they find the culprit. Under the kitchen window, Waldorf is snoring away, with a big tummy turned up toward the sun.

'Just watch,' says Mummy, and she runs inside. She takes a bucket and fills it with cold water, then throws the water all over the sleeping cat. He jumps up, shakes his fur, and runs like crazy out of sight.

That will teach the greedy beast not to steal! Or will it?

TRAFFIC JAM

Here they are, stuck in the car.

What would have been a great outing is being spoiled by a huge traffic jam.

The lady on the radio says something about a huge lorry that has lost its load. The children have nothing to do. They wanted to go to the zoo. But with that lorry in the way....

'Let's play a game,' says Daddy. 'Then the time will go by faster. I'll say a part of a sentence. The next person puts another part of a sentence after it that rhymes with the one I said. That way we'll make a nice poem. Want to try?' The children look out the windows glumly. Their wonderful day is going to be a disaster. Daddy starts.

'The silly Roman...'

Now it's Mummy's turn.

'The silly Roman rides on a bunny,' she fills in.

'Your turn, Lisa,' Daddy urges.

At first Lisa doesn't want to play. But Daddy and Mummy insist, so she gives it a go.

'The silly Roman rides on a bunny, and he feels funny,' she rhymes.

'Now your turn, John,' laughs Lisa.

'The silly Roman rides on a bunny and he feels funny because he's lost his money,' John crows triumphantly.

'... and can't buy more honey,' Mummy finishes. They all burst out laughing.

What a silly poem they've made!

All of a sudden they realise that the traffic is moving again.

'Hey, the traffic jam is over. We can move again.' Daddy starts the car and they are on their way.

Sometimes it's fun to be in a traffic jam....

ZOOM-ZOOM

John, Lisa and Daddy are sitting at the garden table. The children are happily eating ice cream cones that are topped with tiny coloured sugar chips. A bee flies by. Buzzing loudly, it zooms toward the children.

'A bee!' yell Lisa and John together. They jump up in fear, holding their colourful ice cream cones in their hands. The bee hovers near them.

John and Lisa run as hard as they can. The bee flies right behind them, buzzing.

'Help us, Daddy,' they scream. 'There's a bee that wants to sting us!' Daddy laughs. 'Calm down, children. Bees don't want to harm us.' But the children don't believe that. They wave their hands, trying to scare the bee away.

'Don't do that,' says Daddy. 'If you hit him, then he might get mad and really sting you. Wouldn't you be mad if someone hit you?'

John and Lisa stop their wild arm waving. Scared to death, they twist and turn in all directions so the bee won't get their ice cream.

'Bees do love sweet things. That's why this bee is so very interested in your ice cream. They are crazy about honey, too. And you know why? Because it's sweet.'

Lisa and John can't argue with that. They just don't want to share with a hungry bee.

Finally the bee turns and flies off into the blue springtime air. The danger is over. With a sigh of relief, the children return to the garden table. They can finally finish their ice cream.

They just don't want any bees nearby.

CLEANING DAY

The teacher in the school has given the children in her class a project.

'This classroom looks like a pig sty,' she says. 'We need to do a thorough cleaning.'

So today is Cleaning Day. The teacher has all the necessary things in the hall. Brooms, buckets, dust cloths and soap.

She has divided the class into groups. The first group has to clean the toys.

'When we play with toys they get dirty. So give them a scrub with a soapy cloth and then dry them off,' she says.

The teacher gives the children a bucket with soapy water, sponges and hand towels. The first group gets to work, laughing.

The second group will take the toy shelves, desks and chairs outside and scrub them clean. These children also get busy with the soap and sponges the teacher gives them.

John is in the third group. His team will get rid of old stuff. This group also gets brooms, a mop, and a bucket with soapy water.

The teacher gives a hand too.

About an hour later, everything is clean again. The toy shelves, chairs, and desks are brought back in.

See? Even the last chair is back in place.

The classroom looks sparkling clean. But... the children look filthy.

'It's true,' says the teacher, 'you never can clean something without getting dirty yourself.'

LEAKY TYRE

Lisa and Daddy are finally getting to go biking together.

After a while, Lisa hears, 'Pffft.'

She quickly discovers what's going on. She's got a leaky tyre.

'A leaky tyre?' asks Daddy. 'What a pity. Luckily I have just what we need with me.'

He gets a black bag out from his bike's saddle bag. He turns Lisa's bike upside down.

With three little sticks he loosens the outer tyre on one side. To Lisa's surprise, he pulls another tyre out from inside it. That one is black.

'This is the inner tube,' says Daddy. 'The air stays inside it. Except not with your bike, because your inner tube has a leak. All the air is gone.'

Lisa presses her finger on the flat inner tube.

'What does the other one do, Daddy?'

'That's the outer tyre. It protects the inner tube. But sometimes things poke through the outer tyre and make a hole in the inner tube. Then you have a leaky tyre.'

Daddy pulls a sharp piece of glass out of the outer tyre. 'Here's your troublemaker.'

Next Daddy repairs the inner tube. First he finds the hole. Then he puts some glue on it. On top of the glue he puts a patch.

'Just wait until the glue is good and dry, and then we can pump your tyre up.'

A little later the inner tube is safely inside the outer tyre. Daddy pumps hard on the bicycle pump, and before long the tyre is full of air.

'Ready!' laughs Daddy, while he puts his things back in his bag.

Lisa and Daddy carry on their bike ride as if nothing at all has happened.

HUGGING

'John?' Lisa asks.

'Yes?'

'Do you think I'm nice?'

'Of course.'

'Then give me a hug.'

'Hugging is dumb. Hugging is for girls.'

'You silly boy. Hugging is just nice. Shall I give you a hug?'

'If you do, I'll give you a punch!'

'Now, now. Come here.'

'Stop that!'

'Don't be so mean. Just a nice little hug?'

'No way. I'm going to hit you!' John punches Lisa hard.

'Ow! That hurt!'

'That'll teach you.' John punches her again.

'You're just mean. I'm going to kick you.' Lisa kicks John.

'Ow! Mummmmmy! Lisa is kicking me! It hurts!'

'Poor boy. Come here quickly. Have you two had a fight?'

'Lisa wanted to… (sniff)… hug me.'

'Is that so bad?'

'I… (sniff)… didn't want to. And then she… (sniff)… kicked me… in the leg.'

'Come sit on my lap. I'll cuddle you and give your leg a kiss to make it better.'

John stops sniffing.

'Isn't it all better now? Or do you want to cuddle a little more?'

'A little more…. It still hurts a little.'

'Then I'll give you another kiss. Is the pain gone now?'

'Yes, but I just want to stay here a bit longer.'

'Actually, it's good that you understand things better now, isn't it?'

'Uh-huh…'

'I thought that you didn't like hugging.'

'…Well, maybe just a little.'

PUBLIC TRANSPORTATION

John gets to go to town today with Mummy.

'We are going by public transport,' Mummy has explained.

John has never travelled this way. He doesn't know what to expect.

He walks to the bus stop with Mummy.

They have walked by here many times, but John didn't know what it was all about. Some people are standing at the bus stop.

Mummy looks at the timetable. 'The bus will come in less than five minutes.'

'Can we ride on the bus?' John wants to know.

'Yes, that's why it's coming. We will ride the bus to the train station. Then we will take the train to town.'

'And when are we going to ride the public transport?'

Mummy laughs. 'Silly boy, the train and the bus are all part of our public transport.'

'Oh, yes,' answers John, but he still doesn't understand it.

Here comes the bus.

'Put your hand up,' says Mummy. 'That way the bus driver will know we want to get on.'

John sticks his hand up in the air.

Squeaking, the bus comes to a stop. The doors swing open.

Mummy and John get on. The other people at the bus stop get on too. Some other people get off the bus.

'Don't they want to go to the train station?' asks John.

'No, these people want to go to our village. And we want to go to the train station.'

The doors of the bus shut and the bus starts off.

Now John begins to get it.

If you want to go somewhere, you have to go to a bus stop. When the driver comes, you get on the bus and it takes you anywhere you want to go.

Public transport is very handy.

ROSALIE

Today Lisa's class is visiting the old folks' home.
A lady named Rosalie is a century old today!
That is 100 years.
The children and lots of other people are going
to congratulate her on this special birthday.
Even the mayor is there.
Rosalie is a sweet old lady with snow white hair
and lots of wrinkles.
Rosalie asks Lisa to come closer to her. Lisa is
glad to do that.
'Hello, my dear. What is your name?'
'Lisa.'
'How old are you?'
'I'm seven.'

'Oh my, I wish I were so young,' laughs Rosalie
brightly. 'When I was seven, I never thought
I'd get to be a hundred years old. I would like
to show you how old that is,' she says. 'May I?'
The children can't wait.
Rosalie asks the teacher how old she is.
'Thirty-five.'
'That is five times Lisa's age.' Rosalie calls five
children forward and asks them to stand in a
row behind her. That's how old the teacher is.
Rosalie looks around again. 'Aha. Mister May-
or. Would you please come over here? How old
are you?' she asks.
'Uh… sixty-three,' answers the mayor, uncom-
fortably.
'Just think. That is nine times Lisa's age.'
Rosalie calls nine more children from the class
and asks them to stand in a row behind the first
row of children. That's how old the mayor is.
'And who knows how many children must
stand in a row to make one hundred?'
That's pretty hard. So Rosalie answers the ques-
tion herself.
'Fourteen children who are seven years old.
Plus a toddler who is two.'
She asks 14 children and a little toddler to go
stand in a third row.
That's how old Rosalie is.
Lisa stands with her mouth open, staring.
Will she ever get to be that old?

TABLE RUNNING CHAMPIONSHIP

Lisa and John have watched a sports competition on the telly. The athletes had to run around a track. There was a man who watched the clock. Whoever ran the most rounds in a certain time won. The competition was really exciting. Today the children want to hold their own championship.

Unfortunately it's raining cats and dogs outside. They are forced to move their sports inside. That's a bit more difficult, but they are certain they will make it work out.

'I have an idea,' says Lisa excitedly. 'We'll do a table running competition!'

'Table running? How do we do that?' John asks.

'I'll show you, little brother. You have to run around the table as many times as you can in a certain time. Whoever has run the most rounds wins.'

No sooner said than done.

John goes over to the table and gets ready to start. Lisa holds a watch. When the second hand has gone around five times, the time is up.

'Go!' yells Lisa. John begins to run around the table as fast as he can while Lisa counts the times the second hand goes round the clock. Meanwhile, as he runs, John calls off the num-

ber of times he has circled the table.

'One, two, three…, four…, five!'

'The second hand has gone around once,' Lisa says in an official voice.

'Six…, seven…, eight….'

Lisa hears John sink to the floor.

'What kind of athlete are you?' she asks sternly. 'Are you already tired after just eight rounds?'

'No…,' answers John. 'But I'm dizzy from all that running around the table. Can we play something else?'

THE MOLE

There's been a mole around the house on the hill for a few days now. To Daddy's annoyance, the mole has made ten molehills in the grass already.

'That's enough. He's got to go now,' decides Daddy one day.

'Who?' asks Lisa.

'The mole!' snorts Daddy. 'Pretty soon he will start on the garden.'

'Is that so bad?' asks Mummy.

'Of course. He's already ruined my lawn. That mole has got to go.'

'How are you going to do that?'

'Tomorrow I'll buy some mole traps.'

'But that will kill the poor thing,' says Mummy warningly.

Lisa shivers. Daddy can't kill the mole.

'If that mole isn't out of my garden tomorrow, something's going to happen.'

Daddy's words are echoing in Lisa's head. She's got to try to help the mole. But how?

She has an idea, and immediately gets to work.

A little later Daddy wanders into the garden. He sees that Lisa has put signs by the molehills. Each one says, 'This way out.'

'Lisa,' he asks curiously, 'what are you up to?'

'This way the mole will know which way to go to get out of the garden.'

'Aha. And do you really think this will work? It's going to get dark soon. The mole won't be able to read your signs.'

But Lisa has thought of that too.

She sets a candle beside each sign and lets it burn all night long.

When Lisa runs to the garden the next morning, she's happy. The mole has found his way out of the garden.

In the meadow, next to their house, she sees a little molehill. Suddenly a tiny black animal sticks his head out of the ground. He waves a paw at Lisa.

And Lisa? She waves back.

A WRAPPER

It's playtime.

Lisa and her friends are playing tag.

Over by the wall Carl and his friends are hanging around. Lisa sees Carl unwrap a sweet and throw the paper on the ground.

'He does that all the time and nobody says a thing about it,' Lisa thinks angrily.

Carl notices that Lisa is looking at him. He looks her straight in the eyes. But Carl acts as if he's done nothing wrong.

That really bothers Lisa.

Confidently she goes over to the group of boys, all the while giving Carl an angry look.

'Hey,' says one of the boys. 'We don't want any girls around here.'

'Are you scared of girls, then?' snarls Lisa.

The boy is speechless.

Then Lisa turns to Carl and angrily points to the wrapper on the ground.

'Now!' she says. 'Pick up that wrapper now.'

'Why are you bugging me?' snaps Carl back.

'You're making the world filthy with your wrappers. If everybody did that, the whole earth would become a junk yard. If you want to live in a junk yard, then go stand in the garbage can. I bet you'll find you don't like the stink.'

'All right, all right,' mumbles Carl, and he picks up his wrapper.

'Thank you very much,' Lisa says sweetly. Then she turns around and walks away.

Her knees are shaking and she has sweaty palms. But she's proud of herself for putting those dumb boys in their places.

And… she has made the world a little cleaner.

BEDTIME LEMONADE

John has helped Mummy wash up the dishes.
So he can stay up a little later.
Tomorrow there's no school.
He watches telly with Mummy, Daddy and
Lisa, sitting on the sofa. He drinks up a glass of
lemonade that he got from Mummy.
'Mummy, may I have a little more lemonade?'
'I think you'd better not, John,' she says. 'You're
going to have to go to bed soon. You might wet
the bed.'
'But Mummy,' says John as sweetly as he can.
'All right, but I've warned you,' says Mummy.

It is midnight and everyone is in bed.
Suddenly John wakes up. Uh-oh, he's really got
to go to the bathroom!
He already went once before he went to
sleep….

Quickly he turns his nightlight on and blinks
at the brightness. The room is filled with dark
shadows, and outside the wind is howling.
He'd really like to stay in bed….
Scared, John slips out of bed. He hurries to the
bedroom door.
The door squeaks when he opens it.
In the hall it's dark. Outside a moonlit tree
tosses in the wind. Its shadow comes through
the window and dances on the wall.
John would like to climb back under his covers
and feel safe, but he really, really has to go to
the bathroom.
He turns on the light in the hall and runs to
the bathroom.
Just in time, he gets to the toilet. What a relief!
Then he thinks about what Mummy told him
earlier.
It would have been better if he hadn't had that
last glass of lemonade.
He won't do that next time.

PUZZLES

It's raining again. So it's a day to play indoors. The children don't really know what they want to do.

'Why don't you take a look in the chest with all the board games?' suggests Mummy.

The children run to the chest and open it.

Aha! Now they know what they want to do: a jigsaw puzzle.

But not the easy ones. No, they want to make a really hard one. In the chest they find a jigsaw with more than a hundred pieces. That's it!

On the box there's a mountain scene with little houses. In the foreground a cow is grazing in a meadow filled with buttercups.

The children tip out the puzzle pieces. Wow, they have never made a puzzle with so many pieces.

After they turn up all the pieces, the first problem comes up.

How do you begin such a big puzzle?

'Just as usual. We look for all the pieces with a straight side,' says Lisa. 'Those are the pieces that make the edge of the picture.'

No sooner said than done. John looks for the pieces and Lisa fits them together.

'Now we have to look really closely at the photo,' says Lisa. 'There is lots of green from the grass and yellow for the flowers in that part of the meadow. Let's look for them first.'

They get going again. John looks for pieces and Lisa sticks them together.

Then they look for the blue pieces for the sky and the mountains. That works out great. There's only a small pile of puzzle pieces left, and they quickly figure out where those go.

The puzzle is done.

'You know, we should do this more often,' says Lisa. John agrees.

THE BULL

'Way to go, John,' grumbles Lisa.

They are playing football. John has kicked the ball hard and sent it on a long curve into Farmer Pete's meadow.

The children want to get the ball, but there's a huge animal in that meadow.

'That's a bull,' says John, his voice quivering. 'Maybe he won't mind if I just sneak under the barbed wire fence.'

They stand in front of the fence, looking in. The big brown and white beast has meanwhile walked over to their ball. The bull sniffs the ball and starts grazing, unconcerned.

'What do we do now?' asks Lisa.

'Maybe we'd better get Daddy,' suggests John. 'He'll know what to do.'

A bit later Daddy stands by the children, looking through the barbed wire fence.

The beast moos and swishes his tail three times.

'Ha-ha-ha,' laughs Daddy. 'That's not a bull. That's a cow.'

'How can you be so sure?' asks Lisa, scared.

'See the big pink thing under her tummy? That's where her milk comes out. Cows are generally very peaceful animals. You can safely get your ball back.'

John and Lisa still look a bit anxious.

'Okay,' says Daddy, 'I'll get your ball back for you.'

He creeps under the wire and steps into the meadow.

He picks up the ball. The cow stares at him.

Then he runs back to the children and throws the ball to them.

'Oh no!' he yells. 'I've just stepped into a cow-pat!'

But the children aren't too worried. They have their ball back!

ARTS AND CRAFTS

At school there's lots of hustle and bustle, because tomorrow there's going to be a party. The party will celebrate farms, so the children have been busy finishing their animal costumes all morning.

The boys in John's class are going to dress as horses. The teacher has cut big horse heads out of paper. Each boy can paint his horse head with brown paint.

The girls are going to dress as pigs. With their teacher, they have made pig ears and snouts, and of course, curly pig tails. These have to be painted pink.

All the children are busy with their work. They want to look their very best.

The girls are finished first. They can go play now.

A little later the boys are also done.

The teacher looks at the horse heads.

'They look very beautiful,' she says to the boys.

Then her mouth falls open in surprise. 'But look at yourselves!'

The boys look at their hands and clothes. Everything is covered with brown paint.

'You are certainly sloppy,' grumbles the teacher. 'Hurry up and go to the sinks.'

Yelling, the boys run to the sinks.

'Scrub yourselves really well, okay?' says the teacher sternly.

The boys splash so much water that soon everything is wet. Big splashes of brown paint are on the floor.

The teacher gives a big sigh.

'Maybe the boys should have dressed as pigs....'

A PARTY AT SCHOOL

Today is the farm party at school. All over the playground, mothers and fathers sit waiting.

The headmaster makes a speech with a microphone in his hand.

In John's class there's lots going on. All the boys and girls have their costumes on already.

They are looking forward to performing a dance for the parents. They've practised really hard for it.

The girls in their pig suits and the boys in their horse outfits look very colourful.

Outside, the music starts to play.

From their classroom the children see the littler children run out to the playground in a long row. They are dressed as hens and roosters. They tuck their heads down and act as if they are asleep.

The loudspeakers play some peaceful music. The teacher of that class walks around the playground, dressed like a farmer's wife. She looks so funny in her costume! She collects eggs that the little hens have laid.

When that music ends, there's lots of applause. The children in that class leave the playground in a long line.

'Now it's our turn,' says John's teacher. 'Is everyone ready? Then here we go.'

First the little pigs run around the playground, grunting. Then the horses gallop into the playground. All the children do their best. It looks like they will finish their dance without a single mistake.

When it's over, the children get a loud applause.

They have done well.

BLOWING BUBBLES

John and Lisa are blowing bubbles in the garden. They are trying to make a really big one. Daddy comes to take a look.

'Daddy,' asks Lisa, 'would you like to blow a bubble too?'

'Of course,' laughs Daddy. 'I'll show you a thing or two.'

He dunks the wand in the bubble liquid, holds his breath, and with half-closed eyes, slowly blows on the ring. A tiny bubble appears and then it slowly grows to be a huge bubble. Daddy keeps on calmly blowing.

'Daddy, that is the biggest bubble I've ever seen!' cries John excitedly.

A light breeze makes the bubble loosen from the wand. It drifts across the garden. The children run after the giant bubble.

'Oh, no, it's drifting right toward that branch,' squeals Lisa. 'It's going to hit it!'

The children hold their breath. The wind dies down and the bubble sinks slowly toward the branch.

Just before it touches, the wind puffs again and blows the bubble high in the air. The children watch it. After a while, it disappears in the blue sky.

'That sure was a wonderful bubble, Daddy,' sighs Lisa.

'Yeah, and nobody has ever blown such a big one,' laughs John. 'Where do you think it will go?'

Daddy thinks it over. 'If you ask me, it flew right to the sun. The first bubble on the sun.'

'Then our bubble will be famous forever,' says John excitedly.

Daddy grins and gives him a big hug. 'Maybe so....'

SWALLOW POST

A swift-flying swallow is on the way to the house on the hill.

When he gets there, he first flies all around the house. Finally he lands by a window. The bird looks around to see if the coast is clear. Then he wiggles through and goes inside....

'Knock, knock, knock,' he pecks on the door of the elf house.

Tiny Elf jumps out of his easy chair and hurries to the front door.

There stands Victor, the post swallow.

A golden tube hangs around his neck.

Tiny Elf loosens the tube carefully. A letter is inside it. Quickly the elf pulls the letter out.

The letter is from his cousin, Tricky Elf, who is a magician. Tricky can do real magic.

But things are not going so well for the magic elf. Actually, there's always something going wrong.

Tiny Elf frowns. His cousin is asking if he can come and stay there for a while.

'Oh, why not?' thinks Tiny Elf to himself. 'I've got a bedroom free.'

He picks up his big goose feather and dips it into the ink pot. In clear letters he writes that his cousin is more than welcome.

So. Now he just has to wait while the ink dries, and then he can put his letter in the golden tube.

Victor the swallow gets the tube back on his neck.

'Would you please bring this to Tricky Elf?' asks Tiny Elf. The swallow nods. He flies out of the house into the open air.

'I'm curious to see what adventures I'll have with Tricky,' thinks Tiny Elf.

We are too....

RECYCLING

It's very busy in the house on the hill.

All the rubbish and old things are getting hauled out of the house and put into the car.

Daddy has attached a little trailer to it.

Today they are going to the council tip.

They've stuffed the old papers in cardboard boxes. The tins are in special boxes.

The white and coloured glass bottles and jars are sorted into two boxes. There are also broken machines that nobody has any idea how to use, or how they got there.

John runs to the car. He's got his old, worn-out teddy bear, Bummel, with him.

'Are you going to throw him away?' asks Mummy, amazed.

'Yeah, he's all messed up and has lost an ear. And his stuffing is coming out of his foot.'

'But you play with Bummel so often!'

John shrugs his shoulders and lays the old teddy bear in the trailer.

Now they can get going.

Everything is neatly sorted at the tip.

The old papers go into one container.

The glass goes in another container. The broken machines have to be put in a special place. That way they can be handled properly later.

'Where should my teddy bear go?' John asks the council tip manager.

He points out a container to John. John tosses Bummel in. The bear looks at him with tearful eyes.

John stands looking at his teddy.

In a little while the car and trailer are empty and they drive home.

Sleepily, John looks out of the car window... with Bummel close by his side.

BABY THINGS

Mummy is cleaning up.

She has gathered all of Lisa and John's baby things together. The children are curious and come to take a look.

They see piles of tiny clothes and a box full of baby bottles with pink bears on them.

Mummy pulls an outfit out of the pile and holds it up for the children to see.

'You both learned to crawl wearing this outfit,' she says, laughing.

The children look at each other in disbelief.

'What are you going to do with all these baby things, Mummy?' Lisa wants to know.

'I'll save some as mementoes, but the rest must go. We can't save everything.'

'What if we have a little brother?' asks John.

'Or a little sister?' asks Lisa.

'Well, sadly, we won't be having any more brothers or sisters. Daddy and I have our hands full with you two,' laughs Mummy.

'But what if the stork brings a baby to the wrong house, by mistake?' asks Lisa, cleverly. 'Like ours, for example?'

'Yeah,' says John, and he crosses his arms. 'Then we won't have anything for the poor little baby to wear. Then he'll catch cold and then he'll drive everyone crazy with his crying.'

'And if he gets hungry, then we won't have any bottles to feed him with,' continues Lisa. 'Then he'll certainly cry more. We think you should keep these things, Mummy.'

Amazed, Mummy looks at the children. 'Okay. I'll put everything back in this chest.'

The children sigh with relief.

Grownups can get some silly ideas in their heads sometimes!

TRICKY ELF

'Dear Cousin,' says Tricky Elf, the magician, 'since you have let me stay at your house, I want to bake a lovely pie for you. May I use your kitchen?'

'Of course,' says Tiny Elf. Tricky Elf slips into the kitchen and shuts the door.

'What an odd fellow Tricky Elf is,' thinks Tiny Elf. 'I hope he doesn't do too much magic while he's here. I wonder what's happened with his house. He says that it's a little damaged and that the handy-elf needs a couple of weeks to repair it. Oh well, he can stay here as long as he needs to.'

Tiny Elf hears Tricky Elf saying a magic spell. Then there's a loud bang.

Tiny Elf runs quickly to the kitchen. When the door swings open, Tricky Elf stumbles out of the kitchen in a white cloud.

'Tricky, what's happened?' asks Tiny Elf, concerned.

The white elf falls into a chair.

'Ah,' he sighs, while he brushes off the white stuff. 'I wanted to make you a magic pie, but something went wrong. It didn't work at home either. Everything exploded.'

'Exploded?' asks Tiny Elf, alarmed.

'Uh, yes…. Haven't I told you? I made a mistake and BOOM, my whole roof was gone.'

'I don't want that to happen here, Tricky,' says Tiny Elf angrily. 'Promise me that you won't do any more magic as long as you are staying here. Okay?'

Tricky Elf promises.

After that, they have to clean the whole kitchen.

PUPPET THEATRE

'Shall we play puppets?' asks John.

He's found three hand puppets in the toy chest. Lisa thinks it's a great idea.

She sets up the puppet theatre and shuts the curtains while John arranges chairs for the audience. Now the performance can begin.

Only now they have to face their first problem. What play shall they perform? Lisa and John haven't thought about that.

They look at the three puppets. They have Little Red Riding Hood, Grandmother, and the hunter. Only the wolf is missing.

'There's not much else besides Little Red Riding Hood that we can play,' says Lisa.

'We don't have a wolf,' protests John.

They look in the toy chest but the wolf is nowhere to be found.

Then Lisa has an idea. She runs to their parents' bedroom. In the sock drawer she finds what she needs. A brown woolly sock. 'If we can't find a wolf, we will just have to make one,' she decides.

Lisa takes the sock to the crafts table and picks up a piece of paper. She draws two eyes on it. She cuts them out and glues them onto the underside of the sock.

Lisa cuts triangles out of the paper with her scissors. They will be the wolf's teeth. She glues them to the heel of the sock.

It's all set! Lisa sticks her hand into the sock. The sock is now a mean wolf with sharp teeth. A bit later the performance begins. The audience of dolls and teddy bears watches patiently. It is the most exciting performance of Little Red Riding Hood and the Wicked Wolf that ever was!

THE NEWCOMER

Daddy has bought Doodle at the market. Doodle is a very young rooster – still a chick, really.

Doodle is also small compared to the other chickens. But Daddy doesn't see a problem with that. He just puts him in the chicken pen.

Most of the chickens are very nice to Doodle, but Biggie, the old rooster, doesn't like the newcomer at all. With his puffed-up chest and his sharp beak, he chases little Doodle into the chicken coop.

Poor Doodle doesn't dare come out of the coop.

It's night now and the moon is high in the sky. In the moonlight, a thief who loves chicken thighs slinks along. It's a fox.

The fox sneaks up to the chicken pen and digs a hole under the fence with his paws. He crawls through it into the pen.

Biggie, who stays outside to sleep, doesn't hear a thing. But Doodle has heard the fox. Through the door of the chicken coop he watches the fox. When he sees that the fox is about to pounce on Biggie, Doodle flies at the fox and pecks at him with his tiny beak. Biggie immediately sees what's going on and helps lit-

tle Doodle chase the fox away.

Doodle has saved Biggie's life.

Hesitantly, he comes up to Doodle. 'Thanks… for saving me,' says Biggie.

Doodle doesn't really understand what has almost happened. Slowly he turns toward Biggie, the rooster who hated him so much before, and who is now so thankful to him.

'Happy to help,' laughs Doodle modestly.

From then on, Biggie and Doodle are the best of friends.

HULA HOOP

Lisa has gotten a hula hoop.

She's been outside doing the hula all day. She frowns as she sways her hips in a circle. After a while, though, she figures out how to make the hoop swing smoothly around her waist.

When John runs into the garden, he can't stop laughing.

Lisa gets mad and stops doing her hula.

'Just try it once, if you think it's so very easy.'

She gives the hoop to John.

He puts the hoop against his tummy and begins to sway around wildly. After two turns, the hoop falls to the ground.

Now it's Lisa's turn to laugh.

When Lisa sees Daddy, she says, 'Let's see how good Daddy is at doing the hula.'

'Me?' laughs Daddy. Because the children keep insisting, Daddy decides to give it a go.

He sets the hoop in motion and begins to wiggle his hips while he holds his arms up in the air. After three turns, the hoop falls to the ground.

The children burst out laughing. But there's someone else who's laughing from a distance. Mummy!

'Are you laughing at my hula skills?' asks Daddy. 'Come on, try it yourself. Then we'll see.'

Mummy picks up the hoop from the ground.

'Hey-hey-hey…' grins Daddy at the children.

Mummy lets the hoop go and begins to swing her hips. The hoop swings around her smoothly.

'I didn't know you could hula!' says Daddy, surprised. Mummy nudges Lisa.

Daddy and John walk away quietly.

Doing the hula seems to be something girls do very well….

STRIPES

'John and Lisa!' yells Mummy angrily. 'Come here this minute!'

Somebody has made a drawing on a piece of paper that lies on the sofa. The colours have gone through the paper and made black stripes in the sofa.

The children see that something is wrong and come near, dragging their feet.

Mummy angrily points to the stripes.

'Who did this?' she asks, furious.

John and Lisa look at each other. Then John begins to cry.

'Did you do that, John?' asks Mummy sternly.

'I wanted to make you a drawing,' he sobs.

'You wanted to make me a drawing? That's sweet, John, but you can't draw on the sofa. Just look. The cloth is ruined.'

John knows he's done something really dumb. He promises he'll never do it again.

'Well,' says Mummy, 'since you were so honest and admitted you did it, I won't punish you. It's important not to colour on the sofa, but it's much more important to tell the truth.'

John stops crying immediately. Mummy dries his tears and gives him a big hug.

'If you'll help me get the sofa clean, then everything will be fine, right?'

John is happy to help.

Mummy gets some water and soap and together they get to work. The stripes disappear.

When the sofa is completely clean, half an hour later, John skips away.

'What are you going to do, John?' asks Mummy.

'I will make a picture of you to make you happy again,' says John. 'On the crafts table, this time….'

FEEDING THE ANIMALS

Daddy has got a phone call from Farmer Pete, who says he is sick.

Could Daddy take care of the animals for a day?

Of course he can. Lisa and John want to help him too.

A little later they arrive at the farm. Nosey is with them.

Hefty the pig is the first to be fed, with some pig feed and vegetable scraps.

Next come the sheep. They are bleating impatiently. They get hay and sheep feed.

The new animal keepers go to the big stall where the cows are. Daddy brings big bales of hay down and spreads hay in the mangers. The cows love hay. Nosey smells the dried grass, but it's not interesting food to him.

The little calves get milk in buckets.

When the milk is gone, they lick their tongues greedily around their noses. They don't get much more that way.

Lisa fills a bucket with grain for the chickens. She scatters it over the ground. The chickens peck at it with their beaks. Nosey tries a few kernels. He doesn't like it at all.

So, all the animals are all fed. It's hard work!

They can go home now.

At home, Mummy has made pancakes. She's made a special one with bits of meat in it for Nosey. He grabs it and runs off to eat it hungrily. It tastes much better than that strange farm food!

CAPTAIN GREEDY'S TREASURE

John and Lisa are on a treasure hunt.

Daddy has given them a piece of a treasure map that he's made himself. On the map they can see the floor plan of their house, where a dotted line shows where they must go.

It's going to be very exciting!

Carefully, Lisa and John follow the route through the house, just as the map shows.

On the map, there's a drawing of a skull in the kitchen. What will they find there?

When they creep cautiously into the kitchen, they see Daddy sitting at the table. He's dressed like an old pirate.

'Hey, it's a band of robbers! Are you here to plunder my treasure? Get out of here!'

Daddy springs up. John and Lisa slip between his legs and run out of the kitchen.

Whew! They got away from him!

They follow the map to the back door.

There's a cross on the map at that point. Will they find the treasure there?

No. Under the door mat John finds a second treasure map. It shows the garden. Under the pear tree there's a cross.

That must be where the treasure is buried.

As fast as they can, the children run there. As they come to the tree they see a chest on the ground.

They open it, full of excitement. There are sweets inside.

Two strong hands grab them by the collars.

'So, you landlubbers, did you think you could steal my treasure?'

It's Daddy, in his pirate outfit.

'If you give me some of it, maybe I'll let you go…,' he whispers.

The three of them sit under the tree, sharing the sweets.

What an exciting adventure!

HEADING THE BALL

John is playing with his football in the garden. He tosses the ball in the air and tries to hit it away with his head. He saw that yesterday during a game on the telly.

The tossing goes well, but the head hitting doesn't.

Finally John gets angry and kicks the ball hard. It flies straight at the greenhouse where Daddy is working.

Daddy comes out of the greenhouse.

'Say, can you be a little more careful? Your ball almost broke the glass. And you know what would happen then.'

John knows that all too well. Daddy had told the children a hundred times that they have to be careful about the greenhouse when they play in the garden.

John sits down on the grass, still angry.

Daddy comes over to him.

'Why are you angry?' he asks.

John explains that he wants to learn to hit the ball with his head, but it doesn't work.

'Let's see,' says Daddy.

John picks up the ball and throws it in the air.

When it comes down, John almost hits it.

'That was a good try,' says Daddy. 'When the ball comes down, you have to jump toward it. Then give it a hard hit with your head. Shall I show you how?'

John likes that idea.

Daddy picks up the ball and tosses it up in the air. The ball goes really high, then starts coming down.

Daddy jumps off the ground with both feet and hits the ball hard with his head. In a huge curve, the ball flies through the air and…

CRASH!

Oh, no! Daddy has broken one of the panes of glass in the greenhouse!

And John? He understands now how to hit the ball with his head.

DOODLE AND THE EGG

Biggie, the old rooster, and the hens are scratching around the chicken pen, looking for worms and bugs. The little rooster, Doodle, will have none of this. He decides to take a look in the chicken coop.

In the coop he finds some nest boxes. That's where the hens lay their eggs. They are all empty, except for one.

Hey, what's that? It looks like an egg.

'I bet that's a lost egg,' thinks Doodle. 'An orphan egg. One of the hens has forgotten it here.'

Doodle feels the egg with his beak. The egg is cold.

'Poor egg,' says

Doodle. 'Shall I keep you warm? Maybe a little chick will come out.' Doodle climbs into the nest and sits on the egg.

After a while Hennie, the smallest hen, comes into the coop.

'Hello, Doodle,' she says in her funny voice.

'What are you doing here?'

'I'm hatching an egg,' says Doodle proudly.

'May I take a look?' asks Hennie, curiously.

'Of course.' Doodle stands up so Hennie can see the egg. She taps on it with her beak.

'Just what I thought,' she laughs. 'There won't be any chick coming out of this egg, Doodle. This is a ping-pong ball, not an egg.'

Doodle doesn't get it at all.

'An egg is oval, but yours is so round. Didn't you notice that?'

'Uh…,' stammers Doodle, a little embarrassed, 'not really, no….'

'Don't you worry. Everybody makes a mistake now and then.'

Hennie gives Doodle a pat on the wing.

'Would you like to go out and find some worms?'

Doodle thinks that's a good idea.

He's better at that than he is at hatching eggs.

COCK-A-DOODLE-DOO!

It is very early in the morning, and outside it's still dark.

In the chicken coop, Doodle and the old rooster, Biggie, are all set. They are waiting for the sun to rise.

'I bet I can crow lots louder than you,' dares Doodle.

'You? You baby rooster! I'd like to hear that!' laughs Biggie.

Doodle gets himself ready and takes a deep breath.

Then he crows as loud as he can. 'Cock-a-doodle-doo!'

'Not bad,' says Biggie, 'but do you want to hear how it really should go?' Doodle nods and looks at Biggie mockingly. The old rooster scratches the dirt. He takes a deep breath.

'COCK-A-DOODLE-DOO!' he booms.

'Cool!' says Doodle. 'But I think I can do just a little better than that.' Once again Doodle gets himself ready and crows the loudest he has ever done in his whole life.

'COCK-A-DOODLE-DOOOOOOOO!'

Biggie takes a step backward.

'That was strong,' he says to Doodle, 'but not strong enough.'

Biggie strokes his feathers with his beak so they shine.

He gets ready and takes another deep breath. Just when he's set to crow, a kernel of corn bounces off his head.

'Would you two stop that racket right now?' an angry voice demands. The two roosters turn in surprise. The whole chicken coop is staring at them, furious.

'The sun is not even up and these gentlemen are holding a crowing contest. We want to sleep – do you hear?' yell the hens.

The shocked roosters close their beaks.

They silently turn and watch the horizon, waiting for the sunrise.

COWGIRL

Lisa has to take a note to the office for her teacher.

While she skips through the hall, she imagines that she's a cowgirl on a white horse.

Clip-clop, clip-clop, she goes down the hall.

Bravely she holds the note in one hand. With the other, she points her imaginary gun. This brave cowgirl is doing her very best to deliver the note.

But what's happening now? Suddenly she's surrounded by bad guys.

She spurs her trusty horse to gallop faster.

Her footsteps echo in the hall.

She comes to the stairs. Faster, horse, faster! The bad guys are catching up.

Fast as lightning, she runs down the stairs.

Oh, no! Something is going wrong. The cowgirl trips over her own feet and thunders down the stairs. Ow, that hurts!

The cowgirl becomes Lisa, who is crying hard. Hearing all the noise, someone comes to her rescue. It's the headmaster. He helps Lisa up.

'It's not too bad,' he says. 'Your knee is just a bit scraped up. I'll put a plaster on it.'

'And what exactly were you doing?' he asks a little while later.

'I was coming to bring you a note,' says Lisa.

'Oh, thanks very much,' laughs the headmaster. 'You can go back to class now, Lisa. Take care.'

Lisa runs down the hall. Shall she play cowgirl again?

Well, why not? Only this time, without bad guys....

DOODLE AND THE MONSTERS

Doodle is daydreaming in the chicken coop. Suddenly he sees something moving in the brush behind the coop. The thing hides itself in the shade of a bush in the tall grass.

Doodle stands stock still. Slowly the dark shape comes closer.

'Hey,' thinks Doodle. 'What is that?'

The shadow approaches slowly. The thing has two big flaps on its head. Doodle begins to tremble with fear.

'I've got to warn the others,' he thinks anxiously.

He wants to crow, but he can't get more than a peep out of his throat.

He sees that the spooky shape has two long, sharp teeth.

'Oh man,' thinks Doodle, 'they look dangerous.'

To make it worse, he sees now that the creature isn't alone. No, there are four more. They aren't quite as big as the first one, but in the shadows they still look terrible.

Fortunately Biggie comes by. When he sees Doodle, he asks what is scaring him. Doodle points in the direction of the shadows.

'Th-th-th-there! Monsters!' he stammers, in panic.

'Monsters?' asks Biggie calmly.

Then he sees the dark shapes. As Biggie spots them, they come running out of the shadows toward him.

'Ha-ha-ha,' laughs Biggie. 'Are these your monsters? It's just a mother rabbit and her babies.'

'Hello, Mother Rabbit,' says Biggie. 'Are you coming to visit us? I see you have brought your four children,' he says.

Now Doodle sees the rabbits close up. They are certainly not terrible.

Poor Doodle. He thought they were monsters!

155

DOODLE'S RAIN WORMS

Doodle is hunting for rain worms.

He taps the ground a few times with his beak.

'Why are you doing that?' asks Biggie.

'I'm hunting for rain worms,' answers Doodle.

'It's a brand new technique. I figured it out myself.'

Biggie doesn't get it.

'I tap on the ground, so the worms hear me. They are curious to see who tapped, and crawl out to see who it is. But then I am ready and… whoops, I pounce right on them. It's really simple. Tap-tap, wait just a second, and… whoops! Another nice, fat worm for Doodle!'

Biggie lets Doodle go on hunting in peace.

After a while Doodle hears a sound. He stops rain worm hunting and listens.

He hears it again. 'Tap-tap' goes the sound.

Doodle tries to figure out where the sound is coming from.

'Tap-tap.'

The sound is coming from the chicken coop….

'Tap-tap.' The sound is very close by now.

Curious, Doodle sticks his head into the chicken coop.

Smoosh! An egg falls on his head. All of the hens cackle and giggle when they see how surprised Doodle is.

Biggie has just dropped an egg on Doodle's head.

'Ha-ha-ha,' laughs Biggie. 'Is that how you do it with the rain worms? First you tap, then the curious worm comes to look, and then, whoops, you have him. Just like that! Ha-ha-ha!'

That Doodle. He sure was tricked this time.

THE NEST

John and Lisa are standing under a tree in the garden with Daddy.

Daddy points above. 'Do you see that nest?'

John and Lisa peer through the leaves. High in the tree hangs a nest made from twigs and mud.

'There are baby blackbirds in that nest,' whispers Daddy. 'Watch, here come the parents now.'

A black bird and a brown one land by the nest. They have bugs in their beaks.

'The black one is the father,' says Daddy.

'What are they going to do with the bugs?' John wants to know.

'Those are for the babies. Just watch.'

As soon as the baby birds notice that their mother and father are there, they begin to peep as loud as they can. The parents try to share the bugs among the open mouths. When the bugs are gone, the babies start peeping again. The parents fly away to find more bugs.

'They are busy all day long feeding their hungry babies,' says Daddy. 'Toward evening they are exhausted. Happily they don't have to change any nappies, like people do. Otherwise they'd have even more work.'

'But what do the babies do without nappies?' Lisa wants to know. 'Do they go to the bathroom in the nest?'

'No,' says Daddy, 'when they are first hatched, they do, and their parents clean things up. But now when they have to go, they put their bottoms over the edge and let their poop fall below.'

Daddy no sooner says that than a tiny white blob of bird poop falls on his head.

That proves that Daddy knows what he's talking about.

PLAYING GAMES

John, Lisa and Mummy are playing a board game.

It's John's turn. He's got to get a six to move his marker forward. But he's having bad luck. The others are already halfway home.

He tosses the dice. They roll to a stop.

John counts the spots anxiously: only five.

'Dumb game!' he cries angrily, waving his arms around.

The markers and dice scatter and fall to the floor.

'What are you doing?' asks Mummy angrily.

'That dumb game won't let me win!' growls John.

'And that's why you throw everything on the floor? So you can win?'

John doesn't say anything. He just stares angrily ahead.

'You're not very big yet,' Mummy continues. 'Every game has its own rules. You can't win by breaking them. If you can't play that way, then it's better if you don't play at all. And you certainly shouldn't throw things around.'

Mummy lets John think this over. Then he quietly puts everything back on the table.

'Lisa can play again,' says Mummy.

'Can't John play too?' asks Lisa.

'If he can follow the rules and be a good sport, then he can,' answers Mummy.

They wait for John to answer. Will he be a good sport now?

John decides to give it another try.

Mummy hands him the dice. He takes them in his little hands and shakes them hard. Then he rolls them across the game board.

'Six!' yells John. 'Yesss!'

He moves his marker ahead six steps.

Guess who wins this time?

PIE

Tricky Elf, who is Tiny Elf's cousin, is celebrating his birthday today.

Tiny Elf wanted to make a pie for him, but he's been so busy the last few days that it didn't work out. He can see that Tricky Elf is feeling bad because he doesn't have a pie for his birthday. All elves are crazy about pies. Including Tricky. Therefore Tiny Elf has asked Lisa if she'll buy a little pie from the bakery for him. Because you can't have a birthday without a pie.

Lisa comes to his door with a cardboard box.

'Here's your little pie,' she laughs as he opens the box.

'Little pie?' says Tiny Elf in surprise as he looks inside the box. 'Have you forgotten that we're elves? This pie is far too big for two elves!'

'Sorry, but this is the smallest pie that I could find. The baker didn't have any small ones left.'

'Well, we'll just have to make do with it,' sighs Tiny Elf. 'But how are we going to use it all up?'

They think about it for a while.

'You could invite a whole bunch of friends to share it,' suggests Lisa.

'That's not such a bad idea…' grins the elf.

That evening there is a big elf party. There are decorations everywhere. More than 30 elf men and women are invited. They have all brought presents. Tricky Elf is thrilled with his giant pie. He eats so much he almost explodes.

It's the nicest birthday party Tricky Elf has ever had.

THE PARADE

John and Lisa are playing in the garden. Suddenly they hear music and a voice over a loudspeaker. The sound comes from the village. Mummy has also heard it. In the distance they can see a colourful parade.

'The circus has come!' yell the children excitedly.

The circus wagon comes along. Happy-sounding music plays over the loudspeakers. The circus's ringleader, in his fancy red suit, drives the wagon and talks through the microphone.

'Come and see! Come and see! The only genuine old-fashioned circus! An ex-ci-ting show with clowns, acrobats, magicians, dancing dogs, and lottttts more!'

A clown with green hair and a false nose walks behind the wagon. He has a big flower on his jacket and he hands out slips of paper. When he comes

by Lisa and John, he hands them each a slip of paper too. It tells where the circus will be.

'Will you come see us?' he asks.

The children nod yes, very hard.

When the clown sees Mummy he asks her, 'Would you like to smell my flower, madam?' Mummy bends over to smell the flower, but suddenly it squirts water all over her face.

'Bah!' she protests, while she wipes the water from her face.

The children and the clown burst out laughing.

'See you at the circus tent!' laughs the clown, as he goes on handing out little slips of paper.

'Mummy, can we go to the circus tomorrow?' beg the children.

'Yes, let's go,' says Mummy. 'I think that will be fun. But really, if that clown comes my way again, I'm going to run away!'

AFTER THE CIRCUS

John and Lisa go to the circus with Mummy and Daddy.

They sit in the very first row.

The ringleader welcomes everyone warmly. Then the show starts.

The jugglers are first. They do tricks with balls and bowling pins. They move so fast the children can hardly follow.

After the juggling act a clown with a dog ap-pears. The dog can ride a bike.

'Nosey can't do that yet,' laughs Lisa.

Then the clown spins plates on top of long sticks. But his trousers keep falling down. He holds them up with one hand and keeps the plates spinning with the other. The children are laughing so hard their tummies hurt.

After the clown comes the magician. He shows the audience a big, empty chest. He puts a purple cloth over the chest, then knocks on it with his magic wand. When he pulls the cloth away and opens the chest, a lady in a sparkling dress appears.

The lady has two doves in her hands.

John and Lisa clap as loud as they can. That was fantastic!

Here come the acrobats. They jump on each other's shoulders and make towers four men high. They also do tricks on a trapeze. It looks very dangerous. At the end of their act, a man walks the tight-rope across the tent. The whole audience holds its breath.

When the children leave the circus later that night, they say the same thing over and over: 'The circus is way-cool!'

THE JUGGLER

Today John is the juggler at the circus.

He's got everything a juggler needs: balls, bowling pins, and a supply of plates. He got the plates from the kitchen.

First he wants to do an act with the balls. He takes three balls and tosses them up in the air. Unfortunately they all fall to the ground before John can catch them.

Bad luck.

Then he tries the bowling pin act. The circus jugglers worked with three pins sometimes. It looked so easy. John has trouble just holding on to three at one time.

He decides that it's better to try with just one bowling pin.

He throws the pin up in the air. The pin comes down fast and lands hard next to John on the ground.

The little circus performer decides that this might be a dangerous act for a beginning juggler. On to the plates.

The jugglers in the real circus spun plates on their fingers. John wants to do that too.

'John, what are you doing with my plates?' he hears suddenly from behind him. It's Mummy. John is so scared, he almost lets the plate fall. Mummy just barely catches it.

'I… I wanted to play juggler….'

'Oh, but you have to practise to do that,' laughs Mummy. 'Those jugglers in the circus have practised for years to get that good. I'm certain that you should practise with plastic plates, and then later you can use real plates.

Would that be okay with you?'

John thinks that's a good idea.

He practises all that day, until bedtime.

Maybe he'll be a real juggler someday….

TREE

Lisa stands stock still in the garden.
She holds her arms in the air and presses her legs tight together.
Daddy walks by.
'What are you doing here?'
Lisa doesn't answer.
'Cat got your tongue?'
'Daddy,' says Lisa angrily, 'I'm a tree. Trees don't talk.'
'Oh, yeah,' says Daddy. 'I'll leave you alone. Pretty soon people are going to think I'm crazy, standing here talking to a tree.'

A little later John walks by.
'Daddy says that you've turned into a tree.'
Lisa acts as if she doesn't notice her brother and stares straight ahead of her.
John sticks his tongue out at Lisa, but Lisa doesn't react.
'Pffft, you dumb tree,' says John as he walks on.

Who's coming here with his tongue hanging out of his mouth? It's Nosey.
When he sees Lisa, he stops. He goes over to her.
'Woof! Woof!' barks Nosey at Lisa. He means, 'What's wrong?'
Nosey begins to sniff Lisa. He sniffs her shoes, her jumper, and her legs. His wet nose tickles

Lisa's legs. She has to bite her lips not to break out laughing.
Nosey keeps sniffing the whole time. Lisa bends her head forward to see what the naughty dog is doing.
Suddenly she sees that Nosey has lifted his leg.
Lisa jumps away in fear.
'What do you think you're doing?' she asks angrily, and the dog hangs his head.
Nosey was going to wet her!
It looks like Lisa really knows how to be a tree!

164

PRINCESS

Mummy and Daddy are sitting in the garden. John plays in the sand pit. Lisa is in the house. She doesn't feel like being outside.

In the wardrobe she discovers a pink princess dress and a golden crown. Lisa puts them on in a flash.

There's a mirror in Mummy and Daddy's bedroom.

Lisa looks at herself in the mirror.

Actually, she would look better with a little make-up.

Mummy's make-up table has everything she needs.

What colour of lipstick should she pick? Mummy has so many colours.

Lisa decides that pink will match her dress best. She pouts her lips and colours them as well as she can with the fat lipstick. 'Wow, a real princess,' she hears Mummy's voice say from behind her.

Lisa jumps with fear.

But the sweet smile Mummy gives her makes her feel fine.

'You look very nice,' says Mummy, while she looks at the little princess in the mirror.

'But the make-up could be a little bit better. Shall I help you with it?'

Lisa thinks that's a fantastic idea.

It takes a while, but finally Mummy has transformed Lisa to a beautiful princess. Mummy has swept up Lisa's hair and added glitter to her face. She even lets Lisa wear a string of beads. There! The princess is ready. She looks perfect. Lisa gives Mummy a big kiss on her cheek. It leaves a pink mark behind.

'Princess lips,' thinks Lisa.

LITTLE HOUSE IN THE WOODS

Mummy and Daddy are packing some bags. They've told John about a little house in the woods that they are all going to visit.

'It's a lovely house, made of wood,' says Mummy. 'It's in a pine woods. In the children's room there's a bunk bed for you and your sister.'

'I don't want to sleep in a bunk bed!' cries John.

'Don't be silly, John,' Mummy replies. 'Come, help us pack.'

In a bad mood, John finds his teddy bears and puts them in a suitcase. There's so much in the suitcase already that it can barely close. Finally he hears it click shut.

Daddy loads the bags into the car. Now they can go.

John is sniffing the whole time.

'What's the matter?' asks Mummy.

'I… (sniff)… don't want to live… (sniff) in a house in the woods,' cries John, while big tears roll down his cheeks.

Mummy looks at him in surprise.

'Don't you want to play in the woods? You can make a fine campsite with your sister.'

'Well, yes,' sniffs John, 'but… (sniff)… I want to stay… (sniff)… living in our house on the hill.'

'We aren't going to stay there at the house in the woods forever,' laughs Mummy. 'It's just for a few days. We're going there for a little holiday, and then we'll come home to our own house.'

What a relief. Now John gets it. He thought that he would never come back to the house on the hill. If it's just for a few days, then he doesn't think that will be too bad. He wipes the tears from his cheeks. Building a campsite in the woods and sleeping in a bunk bed.

Wonderful!

THE SQUIRREL

The children are taking a walk with Mummy and Daddy in the pine woods. A small brown animal appears on a tree branch.

'A squirrel!' whispers Lisa.

Cautiously, the animal comes closer to them.

'Hello, little squirrel,' say Lisa and John.

They squat down and put their hands out. The squirrel sniffs their hands curiously.

'He's looking for something to eat. Don't we have anything to give him?' Lisa asks Mummy. Mummy pulls a biscuit out of her backpack and gives it to the squirrel.

The little animal takes the biscuit in his front paws and nibbles it almost all up. He doesn't eat the last piece. He takes it in his teeth and bounds away. Like an acrobat, he runs up the tree trunk and dives into his hole among the pine boughs.

'He's going to save that piece to eat later,' says Daddy. 'That's how he gets through the winter.'

'The winter?' asks Lisa. 'Will it last that long?'

'Yes, because squirrels save food all year long,' says Mummy. 'They are smart that way. They have food saved for the whole winter. They even have some outside, under the snow.'

'Can we give him all our biscuits?' asks John. 'We have lots more at home.'

'Biscuits aren't that good for squirrels. Nuts and seeds are a lot better for them. They find more than enough in the woods,' says Daddy.

'Oh,' laughs John, 'then I would make a good squirrel. I love nuts.'

He would look pretty funny with a fluffy tail!

PICNIC

Mummy and the children are hard at work. They fill a basket with all kinds of delicious things they have prepared. Soon they are going on a picnic.

Mummy had made some delicious hot chocolate and put it in a flask.

Daddy has brought an umbrella and a big blanket out from the garage.

As soon as everything is ready, they can go.

Alas, they are just on the way out when thick grey clouds appear. In a few minutes it begins to rain softly.

The picnickers hurry inside.

They barely have shut the door when the storm breaks.

'What a pity,' sighs Mummy, while the rain pounds against the windows. 'Our picnic is washed out.'

'Dumb rain,' mutters Lisa.

'We can't do much about that,' says Daddy, 'but I have a good idea.'

He takes Mummy and the children to the living room. He spreads out the blanket and opens the umbrella. Then he unpacks the picnic basket.

'What are you doing?' asks Mummy, surprised.

'Just what it looks like,' laughs Daddy. 'We're having a picnic, of course.'

'In the living room?' asks Lisa.

'Why not?' asks Daddy.

'Yes, why not,' agree Mummy and the children. Soon they are sitting happily there with their delicious treats, sipping their hot chocolate. Then they play hide-and-seek all over the house.

It was a great rainy day picnic.

GRANNIE'S SURPRISE

John and Lisa are staying with Grannie and Grandad for a few days. On the first day Grandad asks if they would like to go for a walk. The children say yes right away. They love going for walks! 'I'm afraid I can't go with you,' says Grannie. 'My legs have been stiff the last few days. But I will have a surprise waiting here for you when you come back.'

A surprise? John and Lisa can't wait.

On the walk, Grandad asks them a hundred times to walk a little slower, please, because he can't keep up.

They walk beside a lovely little lake. In the middle of the lake there's an old mansion that is reflected in the dark green water. Ducks paddle around. They come toward the visitors to see who they are.

Grandad has brought old bread that the children can give to the happy, quacking ducks.

After that they walk back to Grannie's and Grandad's cosy house. The children run to the front door. If Lisa stands on her tiptoes she can just reach the doorbell. 'Ding-a-ling-a-ling,' it goes.

Grannie opens the door.

'Have you come home for the surprise?' she laughs. 'Go look in the kitchen.'

Lisa and John run to the kitchen. They see a bowl sitting on the table. The bowl is filled with white batter.

'Where is our surprise?' ask the children, a little disappointed.

Grannie goes over to the stove. 'That's what I'm going to start making now. What do you think about pancakes with whipped cream and strawberries?'

The children are so happy! What better surprise could a grandmother make?

PLAYING WITH TOPS

John and Lisa are playing on Grannie and Grandad's sunny patio.

They are playing with their plastic tops. First they wind them up with a string. Then when they pull the string, the tops start spinning on the ground. The top that spins the longest wins.

Grandad comes over to them.

'Can I play too?' he asks. In his hand he has an old wooden top with a metal point, and in the other, a string. 'This is my old top. I played with it when I was a boy.'

'What an old thing it is,' laughs Lisa. 'Do you think it still works?'

'That one surely can't beat our new ones,' sniffs John proudly.

Grandad laughs. 'You know what? I've won competitions with this one.'

'It doesn't look like a winner to me,' laughs Lisa.

Grandad wraps his string neatly around his top. He holds the top between his thumb and pointer finger and wraps the string firmly around his other fingers. With a sharp tug, he sets the top spinning on the ground.

'Shall we have a match?' he suggests.

'Which top will spin the longest?' Quickly the two plastic tops join the old wooden one spinning on the patio. It's going to be an exciting match.

With their coloured edges, the plastic tops bump into the old one. But it spins them away. Lisa's stops first.

Then John's begins to wobble and finally it stops too. Grandad's goes on spinning a while longer.

'I won!' yells Grandad, just like he's a little boy. The children can hardly believe their eyes. Grandad beat them!

A BIKE WITH NO WHEELS

In Grannie and Grandad's house there's a bike that's really strange.

It's a bike with no wheels. It stands on two heavy feet in a room with a closed door.

John and Lisa haven't been in the room before. But today the door is open. They hear a zooming sound. Curious, the children look in. There sits Grannie in a track suit on the bike.

'Hey, you rascals,' she laughs when she sees them. 'Have you come to have a look?'

The children walk quietly into the room and watch Grannie pedal slowly.

'Why do you do that?' John wants to know.

'When you get a little older, like me, you have to make sure you get your exercise.'

'Why don't you just go for walks and things? Or ride a real bike?' asks Lisa.

'I do that now and then too. But if I don't feel like walking, or if the weather is bad, then I can ride inside,' laughs Grannie.

'Do you get tired from it?' asks John, curious.

Grannie nods. 'You bet. You can choose how hard you must pedal. If I set my bike on the hardest setting, it's like I'm climbing a steep mountain. But that's too much for me. I prefer to ride easily and slowly.'

On her handlebars there's a little counting machine. John wants to know what it does.

'It shows how far I've ridden and how fast I've pedalled,' Grannie explains.

John and Lisa stay and watch Grannie. It's weird, watching a bike with no wheels.

Who cares, so long as it helps Grannie stay healthy!

GRANDAD'S BIRTHDAY

The children are helping Grannie make a chocolate cake.

It's going to be a special cake, because it's Grandad's birthday. He will be sixty-seven today.

That means there must be sixty-seven candles on his cake. Lisa and John have been busy for quite a while putting candles on the cake. The cake looks like a pin cushion.

Grandad is not around. Grannie has sent him off with a long shopping list, to make sure he's gone a long time.

'Then we can make the cake as a secret,' whispered Grannie.

Grannie has planned a surprise party. She asks Lisa and John to pretend they have forgotten Grandad's birthday.

While he's out shopping, friends and family are coming over.

The cake is ready and all the guests have come. Now they just have to wait for Grandad.

Finally they hear Grandad coming through the front door.

All the guests hold their breath. Somebody quickly lights the candles.

Then the door to the living room opens.

'Happy Birthday!' yell all the guests as loud as they can. Grandad looks shocked, but happy.

The guests all congratulate Grandad while the

chocolate cake with sixty-seven flaming candles is brought in.

'Oh, my, what a surprise!' cries Grandad when he sees the cake. 'I really thought that you all had forgotten my birthday. So I decided to buy myself something.'

He gets a box out of the hall. In it there's a big strawberry pie.

Everyone begins to laugh.

Now there will certainly be enough for everyone!

LISA LEARNS TO SEW

Grannie is mending a dress.

Lisa comes into the room with her doll, Annie.

'Grannie, what are you up to?' Lisa wants to know.

'I'm mending my dress with this needle and thread. My mother taught me how to do this when I was a little girl,' she answers.

Lisa watches, fascinated, as Grannie slips the thread through the eye of the needle and knots it. Then she puts the needle into the cloth and stitches up a little tear. When she's done, you can't see the hole any more.

'Could you mend Annie's dress?' asks Lisa. 'It's got a tear in it, too.'

'Why don't you do that yourself?' asks Grannie with a smile.

'It's really not hard. I'll help you.'

Lisa likes this idea a lot.

Grannie gives her the needle and some thread. The thread is the same colour as the dress. 'You need to do that so when you finish mending the tear it will be invisible,' explains Grannie.

Lisa tries to push the thread through the needle's eye. But it's not easy.

'Wet the thread a little with your lips,' says Grannie. 'That makes it easier.'

And sure enough, it works. Grannie knots the thread for Lisa and hands the needle and thread back.

Lisa sticks the needle into the cloth, right by the tear. Then she pokes it out on the other side of the tear. When Lisa pulls the thread, the hole closes up. She does this a few more times as Grannie watches and gives advice. Soon the whole tear is closed up.

It surprises Lisa how easy it really was.

Now Annie's dress is fine again.

Thanks to Grannie's help.

LADYBIRD

Lisa sits beside a bush in the garden.

She cups one hand over the back of the other.

John sees his sister and comes over.

'What do you have there?' he wants to know.

'Shhh,' says Lisa. 'A ladybird.'

John is curious. 'Could I have a look?'

Two pairs of eyes peer at the tiny red bug on the back of her hand.

'Oh, it's beautiful,' says John.

'I think it's probably two years old,' says Lisa.

'How do you know that?' asks John, wondering.

'Because it only has two spots on each wing.'

'Then it's just a toddler,' John says tenderly.

Suddenly the bug starts walking on Lisa's hand. It tickles.

'Could I hold him a while?' asks John sweetly.

'Be very careful,' warns Lisa.

John sticks out his finger. The ladybird crawls onto it. Fascinated, John looks at the tiny beetle.

'Won't he miss his mummy and daddy?' he asks his sister.

'Well, maybe he's just out for a little walk, and now he's going back to them.'

The tiny beetle walks over John's arm. 'It really tickles,' he laughs.

'May I have him back now?' asks Lisa. She puts her finger in front of the little bug's head. It stops, then crawls onto Lisa's finger.

Lisa puts her finger into the air and the bug crawls up to the tip.

Then the ladybird opens its wings from under its shell. Before the children can say anything, it flies off into the sky.

'He must want to be back with his mother again,' says John.

Bye, ladybird!

THE MAGIC HOOVER

Tiny Elf is going shopping.

He has asked his cousin Tricky Elf to vacuum the house. Tricky Elf doesn't want to work, so he goes to his magic book to find a word that will make the machine do the work by itself. Tricky Elf is studying to become a real magician.

He's promised his cousin that he won't use any magic words while he visits, but surely no harm will come from this, he thinks.

He plugs in the hoover and says the magic word. The enchanted machine gets to work.

'It's perfect,' laughs Tricky Elf.

The vacuum cleaner is behaving nicely.

After it cleans the floor, it vacuums the table and chairs too. There's no more dust anywhere. Then it starts sucking the cushions off the sofa.

'That's more than enough,' says Tricky Elf to the machine. Just as he tries to look up the magic word to stop the machine, it sucks up the book!

'Oh, no!' yells Tricky Elf, in a panic.

Now the machine is grabbing Tricky Elf's clothing.

He screams and runs away, but the machine chases him.

Luckily, just at that moment Tiny Elf comes back. As soon as he sees what's happening, he runs to the electric plug and pulls it out.

The vacuum cleaner slows down and stops with a burp.

Tricky Elf gets a strong scolding from Tiny Elf. Then he's got to put the house right again.

Without magic words this time....

SWIMMING POOL

The sun has been shining for several days. Inside the houses it's getting rather warm. Including Tiny Elf's house.

Both, he and his cousin Tricky Elf, who is staying with him, feel like having a refreshing swim in a swimming pool. Alas, the elves don't have one.

They decide to go looking for one. Among the odds and ends in the garden shed they find an old pot.

'This could serve as a swimming pool,' decides Tricky Elf, after he checks to make sure there are no holes in the pot.

Now they have to put the water in.

On the other side of the shed is a water tap. It takes a lot of work, but the elves finally push the pot under the tap.

Now all they have to do is open the tap.

The elves clamber up the pipe to the tap. Tiny Elf stands carefully on the slippery pipe, while Tricky Elf holds tight to the back of his trousers.

Cautiously, he turns the tap on. The cool water flows into the pot. They let it fill to the rim. Then Tiny Elf carefully shuts the tap.

But suddenly he slips. Tricky Elf tries to pull him up, but alas, he can't! Together they tumble down and splash into the water.

They come up soaking wet.

'Well,' laughs Tricky Elf, 'we got our wish faster than we thought.'

'Yeah,' says a dripping wet Tiny Elf. 'I just wish I had time to change my clothes first.'

The two elves burst out laughing.

GOOBA-GOOBA-GOOM

One evening Tiny Elf is reading a book. His cousin Tricky Elf comes and sits beside him.

'Have you heard about the Gooba-Gooba-Goom?' asks Tricky Elf.

'No,' answers Tiny Elf. 'What is that?'

'I don't know,' says Tricky Elf. 'But what do you think it is?'

'It sounds like a monster who lives in a dark forest,' he answers.

'A monster?' gulps Tricky Elf, scared. 'And that forest: where is it?'

'If you ask me, it's far, far away from here. In some other country or something.'

Tricky Elf sighs, relieved.

'What would it look like, this Gooba-Gooba-Goom?' he asks now.

His cousin scratches his beard. 'If you ask me, he has black fur, and green stuff drips out of his nose. And he has red eyes.'

Terrified, Tricky Elf covers his eyes with his cap.

'And... and... ' he stammers, 'what does he eat, do you think?'

Tiny Elf stares at his book, thinking hard. 'I think he's crazy about birds and small animals. And sometimes he real-ly enjoys... elves.'

'Oh, no! Oh, no!' wails Tricky Elf.

'But why do you want to know all that, if it just scares you?' asks Tiny Elf.

'I... don't know,' answers Tricky Elf. 'I wanted to know what you thought.'

'Well, I've told you everything I *think*. I have no idea if I'm right. Does this Gooba-Gooba-Goom of yours actually exist?'

'No, absolutely not,' answers Tricky Elf. 'I just made up the name now. That's lucky, because I never want to meet a Gooba-Gooba-Goom....'

Magic Lamp

Tiny Elf is polishing his oil lamp. He rubs it with a rag until it glistens. Suddenly he has an idea.

'Imagine that this lamp is just like the magic lamp in the story about Aladdin. Whenever you rub the lamp, a genie appears and grants you three wishes,' he says to his cousin, Tricky Elf. 'What would you wish for?'

Tricky Elf folds his arms behind his head, thinking deeply.

'That's a difficult question,' he sighs. 'I think that my first wish would be for a castle with golden walls and a diamond throne.'

'That's a lot,' laughs Tiny Elf. 'And your next wish?'

'A treasure chest full of diamonds so that I would be the richest elf in the world. Then I could give everybody presents.'

Tiny Elf nods approvingly.

'And your third and last wish?'

'A lovely princess with sky-blue eyes who wants to marry me,' answers Tricky Elf dreamily.

'Those are beautiful wishes,' says Tiny Elf.

'What would you wish for?' asks Tricky Elf then.

Now it's Tiny Elf's turn to think it over.

'I would wish to get more wishes. You have to agree, three wishes is nice, but not very many.'

'Yeah, true,' Tricky Elf agrees.

'Therefore, my first wish would be to have as many wishes as I want. That way I can keep on wishing for things and never stop!'

'Ha-ha-ha,' laughs Tricky Elf loudly. 'Now *that* is a good wish....'

CAVITIES

It is bedtime, and John and Lisa must brush their teeth. Lisa is brushing away in front of the mirror, but John doesn't want to. Mummy comes in.

'Why aren't you brushing your teeth?' she asks John.

'I don't want to,' he mumbles.

'You must take good care of your teeth, John. Otherwise you might get cavities, and they can hurt.'

Against his will, John picks up the tube of toothpaste. He puts some on his blue and white toothbrush.

'In my class there's a boy who had a rotten tooth. The dentist had to pull it out. When he came back to school, his cheek was as big and red as a tomato. He said it really hurt,' says Lisa.

John didn't know that. He begins to brush his teeth carefully.

'We need to go to the dentist soon too. What will he say if he sees that you haven't taken good care of your teeth?' asks Mummy.

The dentist is a great big man with dark hair and bushy eyebrows. John doesn't want this man angry at him. His toothbrush moves a bit faster here and there.

Mummy laughs, satisfied to see John trying to do his very best. 'Do you know that the dentist gives you a reward if your teeth are in good

shape?' she asks.

That's right! John remembers that he got to reach into a big barrel and pick out a gift.

Soon he is finished.

'Well done. That wasn't so hard, was it?' asks Mummy.

John laughs and shows Mummy his white teeth.

And you? Have you brushed *your* teeth really well today?

VITAMINS

Today it's grocery shopping day.

John and Lisa are helping Mummy at the supermarket. Mummy has a long list with her. They are in the fruit and vegetable section. Mummy grabs a bag full of carrots.

'Mmm, yum,' say Lisa and John.

'Yes, and full of vitamins,' laughs Mummy.

'What are vitalins?' asks John.

'Vita-*Mins*,' corrects Lisa. 'You have to have them in order to grow up, right, Mummy?'

'That's true,' says Mummy. 'But not just to grow. Also to stay healthy.'

She picks up some lemons. 'Look,' she says, 'these lemons give you lots of vitamin C.'

'Is that what it's called? Sea? Like the ocean?'

Lisa laughs. 'No, little brother, C, like in A, B, C. Every vitamin has its own letter name.'

'That's right,' says Mummy. 'In each vitamin there are special things that our bodies need. Lemons have lots of vitamin C, which makes us strong so we stay healthy.'

John makes a face. 'Do I have to eat them? They are so sour!'

Mummy laughs. 'You can get vitamin C from other kinds of fruit and vegetables. Often you get several different vitamins in one piece.'

'So it doesn't really matter which fruits or vegetables you eat,' says Lisa. 'They are all full of vitamins and make you healthy.'

John tells Mummy he's going to eat lots of fruits and vegetables, because he wants to be big and strong. Mummy says he can eat as much of them as he wants.

That's perfect! And delicious.

LONG LIVE COWS!

Lisa and John are visiting Farmer Pete's farm.

A big lorry drives up.

'It's coming to pick up our milk,' says Farmer Pete.

The lorry drives near the milk house, where a big tank keeps lots of fresh milk cool.

The man from the lorry picks up a thick hose from the back of the lorry. He attaches it to the milk tank.

'Now all our milk will go into the lorry's tank,' explains Farmer Pete. 'Then the driver will bring it to the milk factory.'

'To the milk factory?' asks Lisa, wondering.

'Yes, of course,' laughs Farmer Pete. 'They put the milk in packages there so the shops can sell it. Or they make other things from it.'

'What other things?' asks John.

'Don't you two know what is made from a cow's milk?' asks Farmer Pete.

'Cheese!' cries Lisa.

'Yes, absolutely. But what else?' asks Farmer Pete.

'Cream cheese?' tries John.

'Very good,' laughs Farmer Pete, 'but also yogurt, pudding, butter, cream, ice cream....'

'Mmm, yummy,' says Lisa, smacking her lips.

'And then there are lots of things you can't make without milk. Like bread, cake, chocolate milk, pancakes, waffles....'

'But you know what tastes best of all?'

The children shrug.

Farmer Pete draws a glass of cold, creamy milk from the milk tank.

'Just try this,' he says.

The children take turns drinking big sips of the milk. It *is* wonderful.

'Long live cows!'

183

WASPS

Today the children can't go out on the playground.

'We've found a nest of wasps on the playground,' explains the teacher. 'The wasps made it this weekend when nobody was here. They can get angry very quickly if you come near their nests, so we had better stay inside today. That's safest.'

From the windows the children look at the playground. There's nothing much to see there. Now and then they see a wasp fly to a ball that hangs from a branch. That must be the wasps' nest.

The headmaster meanwhile has called the fire department.

Soon a fire truck arrives at the playground.

'There is my daddy,' calls out Sara, proudly.

'Where is he?' asks John, curious.

'That man there, with the helmet,' Sara points excitedly.

He looks very big and strong, with his black jacket and his helmet under his arm.

Sara waves like crazy to her dad. When he sees his little girl, he waves back.

'Is it always your dad who comes to take away wasp nests?' the teacher asks Sara.

'Yes,' says Sara, 'my daddy is a real hero. He saves cats from trees when they get stuck too.'

'Wow!,' says John. 'And does he put out fires too?'

'Yeah, of course, but then he's really careful, because fire is very, very dangerous.'

'That's true,' says the teacher.

A little later Sara's dad gets the wasp nest down and takes it away.

The children have to stay inside the rest of today. But tomorrow they can go out on the playground again.

Thanks to Sara's dad, the fireman.

THE DENTIST

Lisa is going to the dentist for a check-up.
She is nervous. When she runs her tongue over her teeth, it seems like she feels one cavity after another.
Since the last check-up, she's eaten so many sweets....

An hour later she's sitting in the dentist's chair. He looks earnestly at her from under his bristling eyebrows. Then he points a big lamp at Lisa's open mouth.
'So tell me,' he says, teasing nervous Lisa, 'are you a little scared? Haven't you taken good care of your teeth since the last time?'
'Of course,' Lisa wants to say, 'I have brushed twice a day, except for the times I've forgotten....' But it looks like it's best to say nothing. It's not so easy to talk when someone holds a mirror against your tongue....

The dentist picks up a small tool and begins to check Lisa's teeth for cavities very carefully.
'Mmm...,' says the dentist. In her imagination, Lisa sees him finding one cavity after another. She fears the worst. She crosses her fingers so the dentist can't see, under the cloth on her lap.
The dentist is done. He takes his mirror and tool out of Lisa's mouth.
'Mmm...,' he says, teasing again. Lisa is so nervous!
But then he gives Lisa a big wink.
'I'm just having fun with you. They look great,' he laughs.
Lisa heaves a big sigh.
'You can pick out a gift as a reward,' says the dentist. 'And keep on brushing your teeth well, okay?'
Lisa will certainly do that.

A TINY WONDER

Lisa and John spot Farmer Pete walking in the meadow behind their garden.

'Hello,' they call, waving to him.

Farmer Pete waves back. He motions them to come over. They crawl under the barbed wire and run across the meadow.

'Shhh,' says Farmer Pete, 'would you like to see a tiny wonder?'

The children nod, fascinated.

'A calf has just been born,' he explains. 'If you are very quiet, you can go with me and take a look.'

The children promise that they will be quiet as mice.

They creep through the high grass toward a cow.

'Look,' whispers Farmer Pete, 'there's the calf, lying in the grass.'

'Bah,' says Lisa. 'It's covered with slime.'

'That's from the birth,' explains Farmer Pete. 'In a moment the mother cow will lick it clean.'

'Oh, yuck,' say the children.

After a lot of licking, the little calf is nice and clean.

As soon as it's dry, the calf tries to stand up on its skinny legs. Boom, it falls down. But it doesn't give up, and tries again. After a few tries, the tiny animal is on its feet.

Wobbling a bit, the calf walks to its mother. It begins to look for milk. Finally it finds her udder and begins to suck hungrily.

The children think this is a wonderful thing to see. They want to stay and watch for hours, because Farmer Pete was right: this is a tiny wonder.

BRAVE NOSEY

Lisa and Nosey are walking through the woods. Nosey runs happily ahead of Lisa, his tongue hanging out of his mouth.

Suddenly something jumps out of the brush. Lisa and Nosey stand still in surprise. A big black dog springs onto the path and stands there, growling at them.

The two stand frozen, scared to death. The dog looks very dangerous.

When Nosey sees how scared Lisa is, he walks forward a few steps. He begins to bark loudly and to look as fierce as he can.

The terrifying dog isn't scared by Nosey, and takes another step closer.

Nosey growls and barks louder.

The black dog answers by letting them see his sharp teeth.

Suddenly Nosey has an idea. Fast as lightning, he dives into the brush.

'Nosey, don't leave me here alone!' screams

Lisa, terrified.

The black dog comes closer, looking threatening. His eyes are now focused on Lisa.

Suddenly he jumps in surprise and yelps.

A small black and white dog is hanging from his tail. The dog turns angrily toward Nosey. But Nosey runs away lightning fast. The black dog chases him but he can't catch him.

Lisa runs home as fast as she can. When she gets there, she finds Nosey waiting for her, panting hard.

Quickly she tells Daddy what has happened. He calls the animal patrol and in a short time, they capture the black dog.

But Nosey is the hero of the day!

A Place to Sleep

Waldorf the cat has been hunting all night, and now he's dead tired.

He comes sauntering inside, looking for a place to sleep. The first spot he comes upon is the clothes basket in the laundry. There are lots of clothes in it, ideal for a nap.

Waldorf jumps into the basket and looks for the softest place. But before he can lie down, Mummy comes in.

'Darn it,' she cries. 'Out of my clothes basket!'

Shocked, Waldorf springs out of the basket.

Still exhausted, he looks for another place.

With his last strength he climbs up the stairs. Lisa's bedroom door is open....

Oh, doesn't that bed look soft. But he has barely settled down in the soft bedding when Lisa shoos him away.

'You can't do that! Shooo, Waldorf!' he hears Lisa cry.

So he has to find still another cosy place.

He is allowed to sleep on a pillow in the living room, but that annoying dog Nosey runs around there. Waldorf

wants peace and quiet. Absolute peace and quiet. He saunters out of the house again. Mmm, maybe in the garden shed?

As he gets there, he sees the door is open a bit. Half asleep, he wiggles in. A few bales of hay are lying there.

The tired tomcat climbs up on one and looks for a warm, comfortable spot.

But first he looks around to make sure nobody is going to bother him.

There's nobody around.

With a sigh, the poor cat curls up in a ball and finally, finally, sinks into sleep.

THE TEST

The end of the school year is in sight.
The children in Lisa's class must show that they understand everything they have learned this year. They have to take a huge test.
You can't make too many mistakes on this test. If you do, you might have to go to summer school.
Very much against her will, Lisa must study in her bedroom.
The weather is splendid. Daddy has set up the inflatable swimming pool and filled it with water. Through the open window, Lisa can hear her brother splashing and laughing.

Poor Lisa wants so much to play too! But first she must do her addition problems, to prepare for the test.
The problems are very hard. Lisa does her best, but she just doesn't get it. When she finally is done, it's bedtime.
'I think it's great that you've worked so hard,' says Mummy when she sees Lisa's work. 'Your hard work will pay off. You'll see.'

The next day Mummy picks up the children from school.
As soon as she sees Lisa, she asks how the test went.

With a sigh Lisa sets her backpack on the ground and opens it. She pulls a piece of paper out of it. It is the test. At the top, written in red ink: 'All ten questions are correct! Bravo!'
Below that there's a stamp of a smiling face.
Mummy is so proud of Lisa.
'See, your work *was* well rewarded,' she laughs. 'We should celebrate your success! Come, let's get some ice cream. You've certainly earned it.'
And how!

THE OLD WOODSMAN

The walls of Grannie and Grandad's house are covered with pictures of forests and animals.

An old hunting gun hangs over the fireplace, and above that, the head of a deer.

Grandad is always telling Lisa and John about the woods and animals. He once was a real forester.

Today he has put on his old cap and is taking the children with him into the woods. They like that, because

Grandad knows all kinds of interesting places. He knows where there is a fox den. And where the badgers look for food at night. He knows which pool in the stream the deer like to drink from. The children find it all so interesting.

'But what does a forester do, actually?' Lisa wants to know.

'Lots,' laughs Grandad. 'A forester takes care of the trees and plants. If there's a sick tree, he cuts it down. That way the smaller, healthier young trees have a chance to grow big and tall.'

'And does a forester also take care of the animals?'

'Oh, my, yes, a forester watches after all the animals that live in the woods. He counts how many there are. In the winter he sometimes brings them extra food. That way they can stay healthy and strong.'

They walk by a wooden tower.

'That's a forester's tower,' says Grandad. 'It gives you a wonderful view over the forest. Let's climb up there. Who knows, maybe we'll spot a deer or a fox.'

Silently they climb up and look out from the tower to see if there are any animals around.

How nice to have a forester as a grandfather!

MIDSUMMER NIGHT

Today Daddy, Mummy and the children are going to celebrate Midsummer's Eve with a lot of friends.

They have hung lanterns and decorations in the garden. It looks lovely.

The guests come in the evening. There are lots of children, all of them friends of Lisa and John.

The grownups start barbequing while the children play.

Mummy says they can stay up late tonight, because today the sun shines longer than it does on any other day of the year. And that makes this the shortest night of the year. So it's a kind of feast day for the summer, called Midsummer Night. Summer is king.

'That's great! We get to play longer,' laugh the children.

Mummy explains, 'In the middle of winter the nights start earlier and last longer. The sun doesn't shine very long. Then we have the shortest and darkest day of the year. Then Winter is king, and we have a winter festival.'

'That's why in the winter it gets dark long before we have to go to bed,' says Lisa, thoughtfully.

'That's right, you've got it,' smiles Mummy.

But today it's the summer festival. While the sun slowly sets, Daddy lights the lanterns. The garden becomes a fantasy land of coloured lights. The crickets in the grass make the music.

Farmer Pete lights a bonfire and everybody sits around it. The children fall asleep while they watch the dancing flames.

It is a fantastic Midsummer Night. They will surely celebrate it again next year.

DOODLE AND THE FROG

Doodle the young rooster is day-dreaming inside the chicken pen. Suddenly he is startled by a loud croak.

He turns around in surprise. Then he spots a funny little green animal springing close to him.

It is green, and has long hind legs and two big eyes.

'Who are you?' Doodle asks the animal.

'And you – who are you?' answers the animal.

'I'm a rooster,' replies Doodle.

The little animal hops closer to the chicken pen. 'I'm a frog.'

'You really scared me, you know? Because I've never seen a frog before,' says the rooster in a friendly way.

'That doesn't matter. I'm sure I've never seen a rooster.'

Doodle leans somewhat closer toward the frog. 'Do you live around here?'

'Yes,' croaks the frog. 'I live pretty close by, in a pond.'

'Huh? In a pond? That is just a hole with water in it, right?'

'Yup,' says the frog.

'Don't you ever get wet?' the surprised rooster wants to know.

The frog laughs. 'We frogs think being wet is just great. Don't you like water?'

The rooster shakes his head. 'Only to drink.'

The frog doesn't get it. 'Do you live here all the time in this coop without a splash in the water now and then?'

'Yes, I do,' answers Doodle. 'I like it that way.'

'Then I'm happy that I'm a frog, because I'd miss my pond all day long,' says the frog as he hops away.

'Hmm,' thinks Doodle. 'I wouldn't trade my pen for anything, either.' And especially now, since it's just about time to eat....

THE WORM FIGHT

Doodle is on a worm hunt.

He suddenly sees one wiggling on the ground.

'He's mine!' he thinks triumphantly, and moves to peck at it.

'Hey!' cries Biggie, the old rooster. 'That's my worm!'

'No, it's mine,' says Doodle. 'I saw him first.'

'That is MY worm,' growls Biggie. 'I've been watching him for some time.'

Doodle isn't going to take that. 'I've been watching him lots longer than you have,' he replies.

Biggie leans over toward Doodle. 'Oh yeah?' he challenges. 'Prove it.'

'I don't have to prove it,' snorts Doodle. 'That worm is mine, and that's that!'

Biggie puffs himself up as much as he can. 'I've had about enough out of you, baby rooster.'

'Baby rooster?' cries Doodle, puffing out his

chest and flapping his little wings. 'I am not!'

Suddenly Hennie comes in between them.

'Boys, boys, boys! There are worms enough for everybody. You don't have to fight over them.'

The two roosters look at her in surprise.

'If you absolutely must have the same worm, then why not share it?'

'That's not such a bad idea,' says Biggie. 'What do you think?' he asks Doodle.

'I... I think Hennie has a good idea. We do fight over the silliest things. And there certainly are worms enough to go around.'

'Shall we cut him in half?' suggests Biggie.

'Great!' laughs Doodle. 'But....'

While the two roosters have been fighting, the worm has crawled into a hole and disappeared. So the lesson is this: fighting never makes things better.

SOMETHING'S SMELLY

As John and Lisa walk across Farmer Pete's land, they notice that it smells awful.

Then they see the tractor with a big barrel behind it. Farmer Pete comes out and waves.

'What are you doing?' asks Lisa, holding her nose.

'I'm emptying the manure silo,' says the farmer. 'It has to be done now and then.'

'That's what smells so bad. So that thing is full of manure?' asks Lisa, looking at the tall silo.

'Yeah,' laughs Farmer Pete. 'And it does stink, but the smell goes away after a few days.'

'What do you do with the manure?' asks John. Farmer Pete points to the big barrel behind the tractor.

'I put it in that barrel. Then I bring it to the field. Then I spread it out all over the field. That's natural animal manure, and it's good for the plants. Then the plants grow up and we feed them to the animals.'

That makes sense to the children.

'Hey,' Lisa wants to know, 'which field are you going to put the manure on? It's really going to be smelly there.'

Farmer Pete can't hide a smile.

'Uh...,' he says, 'the field right by your house....'

'Oh, no!' cry the children.

But yes. If you live in the country, you sometimes have to put up with strange smells.

196

NEW CLOTHES

Mummy has taken John and Lisa with her to the clothes shop.

They have both grown quite a lot and really need some new clothes. John isn't interested. He'd rather play, but Mummy says he must go along.

First they look around the shop a bit. Mummy and Lisa begin browsing in the girls' clothes. A friendly assistant comes by. Lisa tries on one outfit after another.

Meanwhile John has found the toy corner. He builds a tower of blocks.

After a long while he sees Mummy and the assistant looking toward him.

'Now they're going to start with me...,' he thinks.

Mummy calls to him. He slouches over. The assistant bends down and smiles at John.

'Shall we pick out something really nice for you?' she asks.

She pulls a whole bunch of jumpers off the rack.

The first shirt she shows John has a knight on the front.

John's eyes open wide.

'Mummy, I want that one!' he cries.

'Try it on first,' laughs the assistant. She helps John try the shirt on. Then she points to a huge mirror. John runs over to it and grins as he looks at himself from all sides.

He needs to try on some trousers, but that doesn't matter. He is so happy with his jumper.

'Would you like to wear it home?' laughs the assistant. 'You can do that, and carry the old one in a bag.'

John nods.

He didn't know that clothes shopping could be so much fun.

RUBBISH BAG

Today the bin man is coming.

Last night Daddy was supposed to set the rubbish bag beside the road, because the bin man comes early to pick it up. But it was raining hard last night. He decided to wait and set it out this morning.

But he's completely forgotten to do it.

He comes into the kitchen in his slippers.

'Dear?' asks Mummy, who's making tea. 'Have you put the rubbish out? The bin man will be here any moment.'

Daddy slaps his forehead. 'I completely forgot!' he cries.

In his pyjamas he storms out the back door. Luckily he got the bag all ready last night.

The bin lorry is nearly there.

With the bag bouncing behind him he runs down the path to the road. He waves to the bin man to show he is coming.

But he trips over his own feet and rolls head over heels in the mud, followed by the garbage bag.

The bag rolls and comes to a stop on the road.

Daddy is sitting in the mud.

The bin lorry stops. A helper jumps out, picks up the bag, and tosses it into the back of the lorry.

Daddy stands up, covered in mud.

'Hey,' yells the driver to his helper, pointing to Daddy, 'do we have to take that piece of rubbish too?'

Laughing, the men drive on.

Poor Daddy! What a bad way to start the day.

THE HIGHWAY ROBBERS

Mummy has been shopping with the car. When she comes back, she has to put on the brakes. In the middle of the drive there's a stool. On the stool sits Bummel, the teddy bear. Bummel holds a cardboard sign that says STOP.

'What's going on here?' asks Mummy.

Suddenly two armed attackers spring out from behind a bush. One is not very tall, but has a beard and a curly moustache painted on his face. The other bandit has a handkerchief covering her nose and mouth.

The bandits knock on the car window.

'Get out!' they yell. 'We're highway robbers! This is a hold-up!' Mummy quickly gets out of the car.

The attacker with the beard points an old cane at her like it's a gun, while the other dives into the car and grabs the shopping bag. After searching through it, she pulls a box out.

'I've got it!' she yells to her partner.

'No,' pleads Mummy, 'not the box of chocolates! My children are crazy about them! Please have mercy!'

But the attackers have no sympathy for Mummy. While one threatens her with the old cane, the other comes close to her and looks her straight in the eye.

'We're going to let you live,' she says sternly.

Then the attackers disappear.

An hour later Lisa and John come into the house. They have chocolate all over their mouths.

Do they know anything about the mean robbers? No, nothing at all....

THE COMPUTER

'That looks very nice,' says Mummy.

'Shall I show you how it works?' asks Lisa proudly.

'Yes, sure,' says Mummy.

'Computer, what's one plus one?'

There's some commotion under the box. Suddenly a slip of paper slides out of a slit in the box.

Lisa pulls the paper out of the slit and shows it to Mummy.

The number 3 is on the paper.

'Uh...' hesitates Mummy, 'I think that your computer has made a mistake.'

Lisa turns crossly to the box.

'You are so dumb,' she scolds.

Mummy calls to the children to tell them it's time to eat.

Lisa and John have been busy in the playroom for a long time. When Mummy comes in, she sees a cardboard box on the table. A sheet covers the table.

'Look, Mummy,' says Lisa proudly. 'We've made a computer.'

The cardboard box has a screen drawn on it. Another piece of cardboard has a keyboard drawn on it. A wire is attached to the keyboard, and at the other end of the wire, there's a mouse.

'You're supposed to push out the other piece of paper. This is the answer to the next question. Didn't I tell you that you have to push the piece with the number 2 on it out first?'

Suddenly the cardboard box lifts up in the air. Two legs appear under it.

'I'm not playing with you any more!' yells the computer at Lisa. The cardboard box falls to the floor and John appears. 'You always make up dumb games.'

'Easy there, children,' soothes Mummy. 'You don't need to fight. Listen, it's time to eat. Does anybody want dinner?'

THE NEXT TO THE LAST DAY

It is the next to the last day of the school year. Tomorrow the children have only a half day of school, and then the holidays begin. They can't wait.

It's also the last day of classes they will have with their teacher.

They like him a lot and want to give him a gift. But nobody knows what it should be.

'I have an idea,' says Lisa. 'Let's each write him a letter. In it we can each say what we liked this year. And maybe what we didn't like.'

The children in the class think it's a great idea.

Each child works on it overnight.

Lisa sits in front of a blank sheet of paper, thinking about what she liked this year.

The camping trip in the woods. That was fan-

tastic, she thinks.

Especially the campfire on the last night, when they sang and played games while it flickered. Friday afternoons were also nice. The teacher would take a fat story book off the book shelf and read wonderful stories to them. The children listened, fascinated. When the story was over, they could make arts and crafts projects about it. That was so much fun!

Lisa writes all of this up as well as she can.

'Maybe I can decorate the letter a little,' she thinks.

She picks up her coloured pencils and draws flowers and mushrooms on the page.

Underneath she draws the teacher and writes his name in many different colours.

Boy, they will really miss him.

HOLIDAY

Lisa and John run to the gate of their school's playground, where Mummy is waiting. The last day of the school year is over.

Now the long summer holiday begins. The nice thing about it is that they don't have to go to school. But it's not so nice for Lisa because she won't see her friends for a while. Most are going away on holidays with their families, like her friend Kate.

Kate's parents have a caravan. They can go all around the world with it. Kate has promised that she'll write Lisa lots of letters. Lisa is looking forward to the first letter.

Her other friend, Callie, is going to fly to Spain on an airplane. She's going to stay in a hotel that has a huge swimming pool. Cal-

lie is certainly going to come back with a nice tan. She has promised to bring back a souvenir for Lisa.

Harry is going to the sea with his parents. He looks forward to that, because he loves to build sand castles. He builds huge ones. So he says.

'Bring me some photos of them,' challenges Lisa.

'Okay, I will,' laughs Harry. 'Then you'll see.'

And Lisa? Isn't she going somewhere?

Of course. She's going camping. Daddy and Mummy have bought a big tent. It has a separate room for the children.

Lisa and John have each got an air mattress, a sleeping bag, and sturdy hiking boots.

Lisa can hardly wait to get going.

Ladies and gentlemen, the summer holidays are about to start!

Swimming Pool

It's a lovely warm day today.

Daddy has pumped up the plastic swimming pool and filled it with sparkling, clear water.

The minute the pool is filled, John and Lisa hop in. Splash, splash! They jump and play around. It feels so good in this hot weather.

'I'm going to get two cups from the kitchen,' says Lisa. She steps out of the pool and runs across the grass to the house. A moment later, she's back with them.

Now they can really have fun.

Lisa steps back in the pool. Her wet feet bring in sand and grass.

'Hey, look out,' says John. 'You're making the water dirty.'

Lisa sees it. With a strainer, she gets most of the stuff out of the water. But if she comes and goes from the pool a few times more, the water will be really dirty.

Lisa thinks of a solution.

She brings a plastic basin from the kitchen. She fills it with water from the garden hose.

'What are you going to do with that?' John wants to know.

'You'll see in a second,' laughs his big sister, while she turns off the water tap.

'See now? If you want to get into the pool, you need to wash your feet first. That way we'll keep the water clean longer.'

Good thinking, Lisa!

GOODBYE, TRICKY ELF!

Tiny Elf's cousin, Tricky Elf, is going back home today.

The apprentice magician has stayed with Tiny Elf for a few weeks because his house exploded after a magic spell didn't go right. Now his house is rebuilt, and he really wants to get home. It's been a while since he's tried any new magic.

Tiny Elf had asked Tricky Elf not to play with magic while he visited. He was afraid that Tricky Elf might destroy his house too. That was the understanding they had, because Tricky Elf was such a bad magician.

After Tiny Elf says goodbye to Tricky Elf, though, it begins to dawn on him that his cousin is really gone.

'Here I sit,' sighs Tiny Elf in his chair that evening, bored. 'I'm completely alone again.'

Actually, he must admit, he misses his cousin's company. Tricky Elf is a bit weird, but he's fun.

Suddenly there's a knock on the door.

Curious, Tiny Elf opens the door.

It's Tricky Elf. His clothes are completely ripped up and dirty.

'Uh…,' he stammers, 'you're never going to believe this, but I've had another accident. May I

stay a few more weeks while the handy-elf repairs my house again?'

Tiny Elf bursts out laughing. First, because his cousin is so silly. Second, because he's happy to have his cousin's company again.

HOT WEATHER

It's terribly hot today.

Swimming pool weather, according to John and Lisa. They splash around the whole afternoon.

Nosey thinks it's terribly hot too. He's drunk at least five bowls of water today. He pads slowly around the garden, looking for a cool spot. He's suffering. He looks jealously at the children playing in the swimming pool. He wishes he could get in for just a second, but Mummy says no. What a pity!

At dinner time Mummy gets the children out of the pool. She dries them off with a big bath towel.

From behind a bush, Nosey looks at the empty pool.

Should he jump in? He could, because the children are gone.

Nosey can't resist it any longer, and he runs to the pool.

Splooosh! The water splashes all over as Nosey dives in and prances around.

Mummy and the children look back, shocked.

'Nosey!' exclaims Mummy. 'Get out of the water now. You're getting the water dirty with your long hair.'

Nosey makes a few more joyous leaps in the water and then jumps out of the pool.

'Ha-ha-ha,' he thinks to himself, 'I got a little swim in anyway.'

Mummy meanwhile has finished drying the children.

But that doesn't matter to Nosey. He shakes the water from his fur, sending hundreds of droplets flying in all directions.

Now the children are wet again. And so is Mummy!

Whew! Luckily in this warm weather they will be dry again very soon.

And Nosey?

He loved his swim.

HAY

A few days ago, Farmer Pete mowed the hay in the meadow.

'Why do you do that?' asks Lisa.

'I'm making hay. I cut the grass and then let it dry for a few days in the sun,' explains Farmer Pete. 'That turns the grass into hay. Then I can easily store it for winter. If it's too cold outside for the cows, they can eat delicious hay inside. They love that.'

The hay lies in long rows on the field.

In the distance, a tractor is pulling a big machine behind it.

'That machine will gather the loose hay and make it into bales,' explains Farmer Pete.

John and Lisa stand in awe looking at the giant baling machine as it moves across the field. It sweeps the hay up row by row.

Now and then the baler stops. Then a big gate opens at its back, and out rolls a large round bale of hay. It looks like a huge slice of sausage. Around the bale the machine ties strong rope, so the bale stays firm.

John and Lisa go near the gigantic hay bale and try to roll it away. It's so heavy!

Farmer Pete drives a heavy lorry with a flat wagon behind it onto the field. He uses a giant claw to grab the heavy bales of hay and put them on the wagon. Then he moves to the next bale.

The children think this is a fantastic spectacle and keep watching until the field is cleared.

'I'm glad Mummy doesn't need to use such big machines to make our food,' laughs Lisa.

They laugh some more and run home.

PACKING

'John and Lisa,' calls Mummy to the children playing in the garden, 'can you please come and help me pack?'

Tomorrow they are leaving on their camping holiday, so they have to finish packing today.

'Look for things that you want to take along on our trip,' Mummy says.

The children run to their rooms and begin looking.

After a while they call to Mummy to say that they are ready.

When Mummy comes to look, she sees a mountain of toys. 'Is that all you want to take?'

The children nod.

'You can decide which toys to take, but don't choose so many. Don't you want to pack some clothes?'

Oooh, they totally forgot them. While Mummy goes back to her packing, the children think about what clothing they will bring.

After a while Mummy comes to look again.

'Lisa, it's the middle of summer. I don't think you'll need your winter jacket,' laughs Mummy.

'But suppose it's terribly cold there,' replies Lisa.

'Then take a warm jumper for the evenings. You won't need such a warm jacket where we're going.'

Mummy looks at John's pile. 'That lion costume is good for parties and school plays, but not perhaps for a camping trip,' she laughs.

'But maybe we'll have a party?'

'I doubt it. At least not that kind of party.'

As Mummy looks through the rest of the piles, she doesn't find one single useful thing. Maybe she should have done the packing herself?

ON HOLIDAY

The suitcases are packed and in the car.

Finally they can go on holiday.

'I hope I haven't forgotten anything,' says Mummy.

She's made a long list of things she must bring and things she still has to do.

'The children's teddies?' she asks.

John and Lisa wave their teddies from inside the car.

'Okay,' says Daddy.

'Sleeping bags?'

'In the storage box on top of the car,' answers Daddy.

'Walking shoes?'

Daddy looks through the car window into the back. 'They are here.'

'Map?'

'In the front of the car.'

'Are you sure you have unplugged the television, radio and toaster?'

'Yes,' says Daddy confidently.

'And fed the chickens?'

'Yes, and starting tomorrow Grandad will feed them until we are home.'

'Perfect,' says Mummy. 'I think we can go now.'

'Finally,' sigh the children from the back seat.

Daddy and Mummy get in the car and fasten their seat belts.

'Ready?' asks Daddy once more. 'Then we're

off!'

Slowly, the car pulls away. Lisa looks through the window at the garden. Hey, isn't she seeing something trying to catch up?

'Stop!' yells Lisa.

Daddy hits the brakes and the car stops.

'We did forget something,' says Lisa. 'Just look.'

Everybody sees a black dog with white paws running after the car.

It's Nosey.

'With all the confusion we forgot him,' says Mummy, while she opens the door and lets Nosey in.

'Woof! Woof!' barks Nosey happily.

Now they really can go!

THE EMPTY HOUSE

John, Lisa, Mummy and Daddy are on holiday.

Tricky Elf wants to take advantage of the situation. On tiptoes, he slips out of Tiny Elf's house. If Tiny Elf knew about this, he'd be furious. Tonight he's gone to bed early, so Tricky Elf grabs his chance to slip out. He walks down the silent hall and glides into the living room. There's the sofa. It looks so cosy. Tricky Elf wants to sit on it.

'Lovely,' he says. 'I'm going to stay here a while.'

Suddenly Tricky Elf snaps awake. Oh boy, he's fallen asleep. It's night already, and dark outside.

Tricky Elf sees a dark shape outside the window.

'A burglar!' The thought races through his head.

A man in dark clothing begins to open a window with a strange tool.

'I've got to think quickly how to scare this creep away,' gulps Tricky Elf nervously. He looks around.

On the coffee table, he sees the remote control for the sound system.

With a leap he jumps over to it.

If he can turn it on, then the thief will think somebody is home and go away.

Pressing as hard as he can, he pushes the big button on the remote control.

It works!

The lights on the stereo turn on and horribly loud music fills the house. The burglar ducks and runs away, quick as a rabbit.

Tricky Elf is a hero!

THE PATH IN THE WOODS

John and Lisa watch while Mummy and Daddy set up the tent on the edge of the woods. It looks like it isn't going very fast.

'This could take quite a while,' says Lisa to John. 'Let's look around here a bit.'

Brother and sister walk into the woods, and soon they find a path.

'Hey,' says Lisa, 'let's follow this path.'

'Do you think Mummy will like that?' asks John.

'Don't be a scaredy cat,' says Lisa. 'We'll come right back,' she says confidently.

John decides to follow his sister.

The path goes deeper and deeper into the woods.

After a while John gets tired and wants to go back to Mummy and Daddy.

'We'll follow the path back to where we started,' says Lisa.

After they walk for a distance, the path splits into two forks.

Oh dear! Which fork should they follow?

'Let's try this side,' suggests Lisa.

They walk further along the narrow path, until they come to a second fork.

'This way,' says Lisa, and she takes John by the hand.

A short while later they come to a big rock.

'Oh brother,' thinks Lisa. 'We haven't seen this rock before today. I think we've lost our way. But I better not say anything to John, or he'll get really, really scared….'

Lisa follows the path further, in the hope that they can find the right path soon. She's getting scared now herself.

Suddenly they hear a voice. 'So there you are!' It's Daddy. 'Come quickly,' he says, 'or else you could get lost.'

'Whew,' sighs Lisa quietly. 'Just in time.'

THE SHELL AND THE SEA

Daddy and Mummy have folded the tent up and loaded it into the car today. Then they drove to the coast, where they set the tent up again on the dunes.

'I love it that you can fold up your house and move,' thinks John.

The family goes for a walk along the beach, looking for seashells.

After a little while John finds a shell shaped like a horn.

He picks it up and waves it around.

'Look what I've found,' he yells, proud as can be.

'That's a beautiful shell,' says Daddy. 'Is it a singing shell?'

'A singing shell?'

'Hold it against your ear and tell me what you hear,' says Daddy.

John thinks Daddy is making fun of him.

'Do it, John,' says Mummy reassuringly. 'You'll be surprised.'

John holds the shell to his ear and listens.

At first he doesn't hear anything, but after a while he hears the sounds of the sea in his ear.

'I hear the waves!' he cries, amazed.

'Could I try?' asks Lisa.

'Of course. How can that be?'

'I think,' confides Daddy to the children, 'that the shell loves the sea very much. In order not to forget the sea, the shell hides the sound of the sea deep inside itself. The shell always sings the song that the sea taught it.'

'Daddy, can we take this shell home with us?' ask the children.

'If you promise to listen to the song often.'

They promise.

They wander further along the beach, carefully carrying the shell along with them.

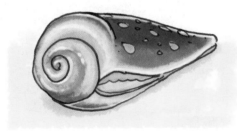

MOSQUITOES

Daddy, Mummy, Lisa and John love camping in their big tent.

The tent has a separate room for the children and one for Mummy and Daddy.

One morning after sleeping in the tent, Lisa's and John's arms and legs are covered with mosquito bites.

They itch terribly.

'I didn't close my eyes all night long because of those dumb mosquitoes,' says Lisa. 'There was a whole army of them in our room.'

'Poor darlings, I'm sorry your sleep was spoiled by mosquitoes,' comforts Mummy while she rubs some bug cream on Lisa's arm.

'I used my flashlight to hunt them down. Finally I thought I had them all. But as soon as I got back in my sleeping bag, there were more.'

'I didn't notice anything,' says John, even though he is completely covered with bites.

'No,' grumbles Lisa, 'you slept like a log, while I tried to keep the mosquitoes away from you.'

'It doesn't look like it worked,' says Mummy, rubbing more bug cream on John's cheek.

'If I have another sleepless night in the tent, I'm going to walk home,' declares Lisa.

'I'll see that you have a peaceful night,' soothes Mummy. 'Tonight we'll put some anti-mosquito oil on you. Try to keep the tent closed today, so the mosquitoes can't get in.'

And sure enough, it works. That night Lisa and John both sleep soundly, without a single mosquito in the tent.

That's good, because otherwise Lisa would have to walk all the way home....

A Dog's Holiday

Nosey is taking John and Lisa for a walk along the beach.

Suddenly he spots some seagulls resting on the warm sand. Barking loudly, he runs after them, and they fly away in surprise. Nosey loves this.

'Here, Nosey,' calls Lisa to the dog.

'Fetch!' She throws a stick into the sea. Nosey bounds through the waves until he finds the stick. Then he swims and bounces back, holding the stick in his mouth, while the seagulls fly around and scold him. Nosey pays no attention to them and runs along the beach to bring the stick to Lisa. Then he shakes hard, getting Lisa all wet.

While Lisa wipes the water off her face, Nosey runs further up the beach.

He rolls in the warm sand and it sticks to his wet fur.

Now Nosey is nearly all white.

Luckily the sun is shining and the sand dries fast. Then Nosey quickly becomes a black dog again.

When they come back to the tent, Daddy has started the barbecue. Nosey runs to his food dish and finds delicious meat scraps. He gobbles them up, making loud noises. He gets a bone to chew on too.

Late in the evening Daddy lights a campfire and they all sit around it. The flames make a nice warm glow.

'What a terrific day, again,' thinks Nosey while he drowses near the fire.

'As far as I'm concerned, every day should be a holiday.'

THE FISH MARKET

'Let's all go to the fish market,' suggests Daddy this morning as they have breakfast.

'That's where the fishermen sell their fresh-caught fish. You can't get them any fresher,' explains Mummy.

Soon the family is walking through the fish market.

The whole square smells like fresh fish. Fishermen are calling to customers and selling their catch. John and Lisa's eyes open wide when they see all the different kinds of fish. There are short and long ones, fat and thin, flat and round. Some are grey, others black, and others brown or even red.

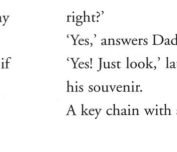

'Do they catch whales here?' John asks Daddy.

Daddy laughs. 'I don't think that they have any around here.'

'Oh, too bad,' says John. 'I would buy one if they did.'

Lisa is over by a stand that doesn't have a single fish. Instead, it's full of shellfish.

'All the creatures who wear their houses, like mussels, oysters and snails, are sold here,' explains Mummy

'Yikes,' cries Lisa. 'People eat snails?'

'Oh my yes,' laughs Mummy. 'They taste delicious.'

'That could be,' says Lisa, 'but you don't need to buy any for me. Ugh.'

At the end of the fish market there's a souvenir stand. The children can each pick one thing out.

Meanwhile, Daddy comes up, carrying some crabs and lobsters by their tails.

'Daddy? You said they don't sell whales here, right?'

'Yes,' answers Daddy. 'Did you think they did?'

'Yes! Just look,' laughs John. He shows Daddy his souvenir.

A key chain with a plastic whale attached….

PARTY IN THE CHICKEN COOP

Doodle waits impatiently for mealtime to come.

A car drives up. An older man steps out. It's Grandad, who's come to feed the chickens.

'He's here! He's here!' cries Doodle excitedly. With that the whole chicken pen explodes with noise.

All the chickens come running and clucking, to look at Grandad.

'Yes, yes! He has a sack with him! Yippee!' cries Hennie the hen, which makes all the other hens cackle even louder.

Grandad disappears into the garden shed.

'Are they going to be away on holiday for very long?' Doodle asks Biggie, the old rooster.

'Usually a week or two,' answers Biggie.

'During that time Grandad feeds us, and it's a two-week-long party. Grandad always gives us more food than Daddy. And he brings an extra sack of vegetable scraps with him too.'

'That's lucky,' says Violet the hen, 'because I am sure I've gained some weight from all that grain. I'm just going to eat vegetables today.'

Grandad walks into the chicken pen. The chickens push and shove each other, trying to be in the first row.

There's a deafening commotion in the pen.

Grandad sprinkles the grain on the ground. The hens and roosters begin to peck like crazy. Nobody holds back.

Then Grandad grabs the sack with vegetable scraps and scatters them around.

'What a feast,' cackles Violet. 'Salad, carrots, tomatoes, cucumbers….That's wonderful.'

Grandad watches, smiling, while the chickens fill their tummies. Then he leaves the chicken pen to go home.

'Bye, chickens. Until tomorrow. I'll bring you some more vegetable scraps then.'

It's going to be another feast all over again!

A BAD SMELL

'Bah! What a stink!' says Lisa as she walks up to the tent. 'What's it coming from?'

Then she hesitates… should she go into the tent after all? She really needs to go to the bathroom. The toilets at the campground don't have toilet paper in them. The campers have to bring their own with them each time. Lisa must get her roll, but it's at the back of the tent, in her backpack.

She pinches her nose shut and holds her breath. Then she dashes into the tent. With her cheeks bulging with air, she looks like she's about to go diving.

'Actually, that's true,' she thinks. 'It's just that I'm diving into a tent that smells awful.'

She creeps along the camping beds to her backpack. It hangs on a string. There's no toilet paper in it. Darn, where did she leave it? Her breath is almost gone. Oh no – is she going to have to breathe? She can't hold it in any longer. Gasping, she takes a breath. What stinks so badly?

Then she discovers where the smell is coming from.

It's John's socks, lying under his camp bed.

'Oh my, what stinky socks!' she exclaims. 'If you ask me, John must have worn them for several days. If I tell Mummy about this…'

With a stick, Lisa snags the awful socks and carries them outside.

It doesn't smell so bad in the tent now.

She wraps them up fast.

Finally she can go to the bathroom.

SPAGHETTI

Mummy sits at a little table in front of the tent, slicing vegetables.

'When are we going to have spaghetti again?' asks John.

'Today,' answers Mummy. 'I'm cutting the vegetables for the sauce now. Are you hungry for spaghetti?' John is crazy about it.

'Will it taste as good as it does at home?' John asks hungrily.

'Of course,' laughs Mummy. 'I'll put in exactly the same ingredients.'

'Ingre… what?' asks John.

'I mean, I'll put in the same things that I do when we're home. Vegetables, meat and herbs. Why do you ask?'

'Because you don't have a kitchen here,' says John.

'Oh, but I have everything I need. A gas stove, two pots, this table, and some water. It will be just fine.'

When the vegetables are all cut up Mummy begins to cook them.

She takes the second pot and pours water into it from a plastic jug. Then she sets it on the gas stove.

Soon the two pots are simmering.

Mummy puts the dry spaghetti in the pan filled with water and stirs the sauce.

She and John set the little table. She puts on the plates and John does the silverware.

When everything is cooked, they all sit down to eat.

Curious, John watches while Mummy puts spaghetti on her plate and spoons on some sauce.

The sauce looks and smells the same. Time to try it and see if it tastes the same too.

Cautiously, John takes a bite.

'So, John? Is it just as delicious as at home?'

A big smile breaks across his face.

'Even more delicious!' he beams.

THE PLAYGROUND

There are several children staying at the campsite.

Lisa and John play with them a lot at the playground.

There are children from other countries who speak different languages. But that's not a problem. Every child can play tag or hide and seek. You don't need words for that.

At first it was a little awkward, but after the first game, the ice was broken.

The children realise that for some things they use the same word, even though they speak a different language.

'Shokolahdah,' says Johan, from Germany.

'Shokola,' says Pierre, from France.

'Shokolatay, says Maria, from Spain.

They teach each other words, and bit by bit they understand each other better.

Sometimes they double over with laughter when somebody says something really funny. Or if somebody tries to say a word from another language, but doesn't do it very well.

They quickly become best friends, playing from morning until night around the campground.

If there's something that they can't explain very well, they draw a picture on a piece of paper. It's a little like a game.

They exchange addresses. Then when they get home, they can write to each other.

'If grownups could be this nice to each other,' thinks Lisa, 'we wouldn't have any wars.'

WRITING LETTERS

Mummy has bought some postcards. She will send them to Grannie and Grandad, Aunt Bonnie and Uncle Bob, and several other friends. That way everyone can see how beautiful it is where they are camping.

Mummy and Lisa start writing.

'What shall I write?' Lisa asks Mummy.

'That it's beautiful here, or that it's fun here. Whatever you want.'

With a pen in her mouth, Lisa thinks about what to write on her first card. It's for Grannie and Grandad. The she writes in her best handwriting: 'Dear Grannie and Grandad, we have had a lot of fun already on our holiday. The weather is beautiful. John and I love sleeping in the tent. Hugs and kisses, Lisa.'

'That's well done,' says Mummy. 'You didn't make a single mistake.'

Lisa laughs proudly. 'What shall I write on the other cards?'

'Why don't you write the same thing? It won't matter if you do,' says Mummy.

'Yeah, why not,' thinks Lisa, and she begins to write the other cards.

John can also write his name on the cards.

Mummy has written his name on a piece of paper. He just has to copy it as well as he can. It's not easy, but he does a good job.

John gets to put the stamps on the cards.

So there! The cards are done. They can get posted. Luckily it's not a long walk to the post box.

The children take turns putting the cards into the post box.

Writing postcards is really fun. Especially if you can write them yourself.

THE CAT CONCERT

Waldorf the cat is going out for the evening, because it's a warm night.

He walks near the little square behind the butcher's shop.

All the cats of the village come there every evening.

As he comes to the square, he looks for a good spot on a high wall.

A big white cat strolls into the square. She stops under the streetlight, so it looks like she's standing under a spotlight.

'Good evening, cats and tom cats,' she says formally, 'welcome to our summer evening concert. Tonight our best singers are going to sing some of our most beautiful songs for you. I hope you will enjoy it.'

The cat disappears from the spotlight.

Two other cats step out from behind a rubbish bin into the pool of light.

They start singing a beautiful tune.

The other cats listen, charmed. When the song is over, they give it loud applause.

With deep bows, the singers accept the applause.

Just as the applause dies out, they start their second song. They sing a splendid aria in full voice.

Suddenly something sails through the air towards the two singers. They barely escape getting hit.

It's the butcher's shoe.

'Your caterwauling is over!' he yells angrily. 'Every summer evening it's the same song. All the cats in the village come and howl. It's driving me crazy!'

The cats all disappear. The concert is over for tonight.

People just don't seem to like cat concerts.

THE LAST NIGHT

This is the last night that John and Lisa get to sleep in their tent. Tomorrow they will take it down and drive home.

John and Lisa lie in their camp beds.

'What a pity,' sighs Lisa. 'I wish we could stay a few more weeks….'

'I would stay a whole year,' answers John.

His sister laughs. 'I think that it would be pretty cold in the tent in the winter.'

'Mmm,' says John. 'That's probably true. I'd rather be in our warm house on the hill then.'

'And in a tent there isn't any telly,' continues Lisa.

'But who cares? There were so many children to play with.'

'Yes, but after school starts there won't be any kids here at all, and you'd be all alone. And no telly either.'

Suddenly Lisa has a great idea.

'Maybe we can set up the tent again at home?'

'That would be fun,' laughs John. 'Then we can camp all year long.'

'Yes,' says Lisa. 'And we can sleep in the tent too.'

'And,' adds John, 'if we want to watch telly, we can go inside. We'll never be bored, because our friends live nearby.'

Lisa has another idea. 'If the winter gets too cold, we can take our heavy jumpers out of the wardrobe.'

Suddenly they hear a voice speak sternly.

'Children, it's very late. Stop talking and get to sleep.'

John and Lisa look at each other and laugh.

Then they turn over and dream of a lovely tent in the garden.